LITTLE CALF

LITTLE CALF

Adapted from THE YEAR OF THE WHALE

By Victor B. Scheffer

Decorations by LEONARD EVERETT FISHER

Published by Charles Scribner's Sons   New York

Contents

Introduction

This story of a sperm whale is fiction based on fact. Some of the human characters that appear in it are real, if disguised; others are not real, though they could be. The other whales, the porpoises and dolphins, the fishes and squids, the seabirds, the weather, the kinds of ships, the floating wreckage, the icebergs, and the oceanic islands belong to the environment of a sperm whale.

Each chapter is named for a month of the year. The decoration by Leonard Everett Fisher that opens each chapter shows the zodiacal constellation of that month and a different activity of the Little Calf and his companions as described in the text. So the sky of September shows Libra; October, Scorpius; November, Sagittarius; December, Capricornus; January, Aquarius; February, Pisces; March, Aries; April, Taurus; May, Gemini; June, Cancer; July, Leo; and August, Virgo. The frontispiece shows some winter constellations visible in the Northern Hemisphere—Andromeda and Pegasus. These decorations are not meant as an astronomical

7

chart of the heavens but are purely ornamental, expressing the mystery and wildness of a whale's life.

Why have I written about the sperm whale in particular? Partly because it is quickly identified by the whale hunters and is not confused with other species; the many eyewitness stories of its peculiar habits are unusually reliable.

It is large (up to sixty feet); it has no back fin; it has a huge squarish head almost one-third the length of its body, and a single nostril, which means that it gives off only one spout with each breath. These features are clearly marked.

Its body "can be compared to little else than a dark rock, or the bole of some giant tree," wrote Frederick D. Bennett, in his *Narrative of a Whaling Voyage around the Globe from the Year 1833 to 1836.*

The sperm whale is cosmopolitan. It roams through all the wild seas of the world except those within the icy borders of the Arctic and Antarctic. Because it is wide-ranging, the chances of finding and studying stranded specimens are correspondingly rich.

The sperm whale has held for mankind a special, mystical meaning ever since Herman Melville wrote *Moby-Dick* in 1851. Moving through a dim, dark, cool, watery world of its own, the whale is timeless and ancient; part of our common heritage and yet remote, awful, prowling the ocean floor a half-mile down, under the guidance of powers and senses we are only beginning to grasp.

No man can say that he has probed deeply into the natural history of this whale or any whale. And indeed how could he? How could he follow a whale on the high seas through a yearly migration that may—in the example of the gray whale—circle for nine thousand miles, at one extreme among ice floes and at the other under a burning Mexican sun?

The whale biologist does the best he can. He scrapes a film of alga scum from the back of a harpooned animal towed to a whaling station and surmises that the animal had recently lived in colder waters, where this kind of alga is known to flourish. He slices the ovaries of a whale, counts the scars of pregnancy, and reconstructs in imagination the reproductive history and age of the beast. Or he counts the ripple marks on the roots of the teeth, or on the whalebone plates, or on the earwax plug, as a forester counts rings on the butt of a tree, and arrives at another estimate of age. He reads that a sperm whale has tangled in a telephone cable on the sea floor at a depth of over three thousand feet, and he gets new insight into the astounding diving ability of the whale.

On such evidence the science of cetology, or whale lore, has been erected. It deals not only with whales but with their smaller relatives the dolphins and porpoises. All are mammals, warm-blooded, giving milk, breathing air. The larger species are known as whales; among the smaller species those with sharp snouts are usually called dolphins, those with blunt heads porpoises. There is a unique species called the narwhal, which has only one tooth, a spiral tusk up to eight feet long, but since this species lives in Arctic waters only, its members do not cross the path of the sperm whales.

In describing the lives of a little sperm whale and his companions I have drawn on the best and newest information. However, zoologists are still uncertain about the reproductive cycle, the rate of body growth, and many other aspects of the biology of the species. The four-year cycle of reproduction seems to be most common; that is, the breeding female gives birth to a calf only once in four years. The growth rate will be understood only when we have better methods of estimating age. The light and dark layers of ivory that are visible in the teeth of the whale are surely correlated with age, though whether two or four layers are deposited each year is a moot question. The two-layer plan seems to fit the growth rate of North Pacific sperm whales. It means that both male and female whales reach sexual maturity at about age nine, full body size at perhaps age thirty to forty-five, and extreme old age at seventy-five years.

It is difficult to think about whales without thinking about men; the devoted men who study whales and whaling over the world and who write about them in a dozen languages. As I write about one particular whale, I try to show, too, how men feel about whales and what they do to whales, and what whales do to men.

The story of the Little Calf starts with his birth, in a quiet month in autumn in the northeastern Pacific Ocean.

SEPTEMBER

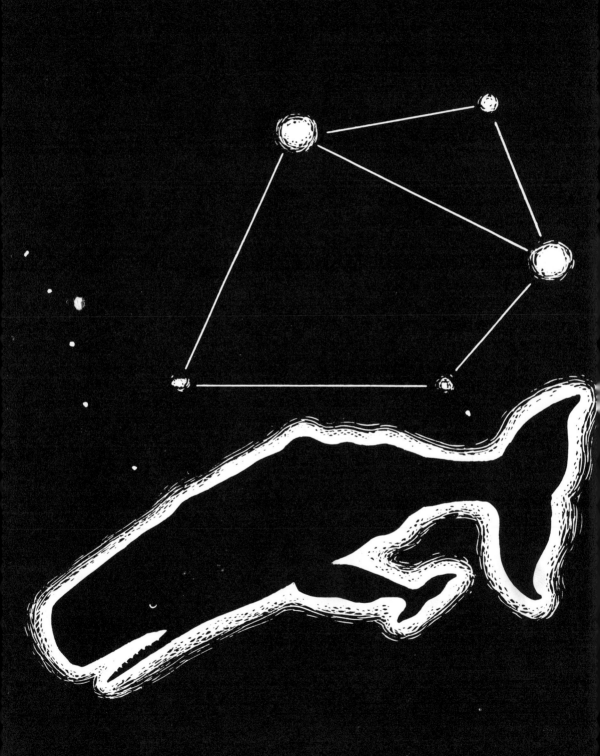

IT is early September when for the first time the Little Calf sees light—a blue-green, dancing light. He slips easily from his mother's body beneath the surface of the Pacific Ocean two hundred miles west of Mexico, on the Tropic of Cancer. He trembles, for the water is cold and he has lain for sixteen months in a warm chamber at ninety-six degrees. He gasps for air as his mother nudges him anxiously to the surface with her broad snout. He breathes rapidly and desperately for a while, puffing with each breath a small cloud of vapor down the autumn breeze.

The sky above vibrates with a piercing clarity that we who live in the shadow of city smoke have long forgotten. Scattered over the riffled surface of the water as far as the eye can see are small groups of whales. A black back rolls slowly in the sun and glistens for an instant as it disappears. Vapor plumes rise and dissolve in the distance. An occasional *thwack* like a rifle shot breaks the calm, its source a mystery, perhaps a love pat or a mock battle between cavorting youngsters. No bird is in the air, but suddenly, as if by magic, an albatross appears and drops heavily to the water, tearing the surface for twenty yards with its broad webbed feet. It has sighted a fresh, purple-red placenta. Here, on the calving grounds of the sperm whale, the season of birth is at its height.

Whales share with sea cows (manatees and dugongs) and

13

with the hippopotamus of Africa the distinction of being the only mammals born under water. The Little Calf is born tail first, like all young whales, though most human babies, calves, and colts are born head first. Because of his tadpole shape, large head, stiff neck, and long tapering rear, he has no choice but to back into the outer world. There is no time to spare in his birth and no time to correct a mistake. Only for a moment is the baby whale in danger of being trapped in the birth passage or choked by the five-foot umbilical cord.

As mother and calf roll in the wash the cord snaps. The baby opens a pink mouth with knobby, toothless gums and seems suddenly to smile, for the upturned corners of his mouth break into a satisfied smirk. This is illusion, of course; the smile of a whale is a built-in feature with which it is endowed at birth and retains throughout life. A land creature may yawn and snarl and frown, may screw up its forehead and grow wrinkled in old age; the face of the whale stays round and firm—expressionless but for the rolling of the eyes and the clapping of the jaws.

In body form the Little Calf is shapely like his mother, though his tail flukes are pale and crumpled and folded at the corners. While in the womb he had lain like a bent bow, his back arched. Now he is straight and supple. He is almost black, with splotches of white and gray on his slick, rubbery body.

Most whales are in fact dressed in monotonous patterns of black, gray, and white, relieved here and there with faint washes of pink or yellowish. They have no need for brighter coloring, since, as far as anyone knows, they have poor color vision.

In the meantime, off to the north, twenty pilot whales come roistering in with soft explosions, all abreast like troopers. Their foaming wake and the *chuff-chuff-chuff* of their breathing startle the Little Calf. He presses to his mother's side. She makes no move, and the school tumbles on toward the horizon. Had these been killer whales, though, she would have sensed the special underwater sounds of the raiders a mile or more away and would have been ready for battle.

The members of the family of the Little Calf are cruising in a wide circle which will bring them back in a week to the same spot. Here and there a whale rests at the surface with full stomach, while others move ahead. A triangle tail rises high in the air for a moment as a whale gains momentum for his long descent, or "sound." The placid water roils at the scene of a petty skirmish between two jealous mothers, each with newborn calf. In the still air of the afternoon the little sounds are few and far between, like the whisperings of a desert land, though the sea below is all aquiver with subdued noise—the ultrasounds of a thousand whales communicating with one another and holding their group together by invisible cords. The whales forge slowly ahead, feeding and loafing and playing, quarreling a bit but leading in general a quiet life. The time of excitement is six full months away—the season of courtship.

On his first day of life the Little Calf blunders round and round his mother's body, seeking blindly for the place he finally finds: a soft spot that tastes good when he nuzzles it. Each of the mother's two nipples is hidden in a deep slit, one on each side of the belly, far behind the navel. He works his

15

little mouth into position and presses hard; his mother responds by extruding one nipple at a time and squirting a strong flow of milk against the back of his throat. Occasionally the mother turns on her side, with her breast nearly out of the water while the calf, lying parallel with his head in the same direction, holds the teat sideways in the angle of his jaw with his snout protruding from the surface. Such an arrangement seems very awkward, for the Little Calf has no real lips and his lower jaw is narrow, underslung, and twenty inches long.

In his first struggle to nurse, the Little Calf is hindered by a grown female playing the role of "auntie." She lost her own calf by miscarriage in July. With the keen sense of group solidarity of sperm whales, she senses that something is wrong. She glides up to the pair and time and again places her long body between mother and calf. Each time, she is repulsed with a blow from the mother's flukes. She finally moves to a safe distance and listens to the submarine click-talk between the pair, the tones of the mother strong and steady, those of the baby weak and experimental.

For two years the Little Calf will continue to suck at his mother's belly, rising and dipping near the surface of the sea in the long Pacific swell. He follows his mother like a shadow and grows rapidly on his diet of thick milk, over one-third of it pure fat. (The blue dairy milk delivered to my doorstep each morning contains only four percent fat.) His coat of blubber is only an inch thick at first, and during the first few weeks he shivers in the chill of the sea. He will grow steadily throughout the long suckling period, gaining an average of seven pounds a day. Many years hence his blubber coat will have developed into a great firm blanket more than a foot thick.

By the end of September the Little Calf is able to match

the speed of his family. When a Panama freighter comes throbbing near, alarming the group, he leaps actively beside his mother, spouting freely, keeping up well with the rapid pace of the retreating party. One of the half-grown males bursts clear of the water and floats for an instant against the dark blue sky before he twists in midair and crashes on his side in a glorious fountain of white. Another catches the spirit and breaches four times in a row; he finally coasts along near the surface, tired but content.

But the Little Calf does not fare so well one morning in late September when the sky turns black and sullen, the wind rises, and the fringes of the waves begin to tear away in ragged sheets. The chatter of his family is lost to him in the scream of the gale. One moment beside his mother, at the next he is lifted in a smother of foam, then down a dark, dizzy, sliding trough deep into the sea before he can gasp for breath or clear his nose. His mother senses the trouble and makes a lee for him with her great, comforting back. He spouts air and water for several minutes, then breathes more freely, falls in with the smashing rhythm of the seas, and feels secure. All that day and night his mother stays with him.

Ordinarily, she would have made a dozen or more deep dives during the night to feast on fish and squid. This she must do to replenish her milk supply. It is no hardship, though, for her to fast for a night, for like all whales she can go for weeks without food, living on the reserve fat in her body. Not content perhaps, she is accepting, suffused with what we humans call mother love. Like many a denizen of the open sea she has ridden out a hundred storms, wherein to feed or try to feed would be more painful than simply to wait.

The sky clears in the new dawn. The members of the family convene and begin to doze or play under the warm rays of the sun. A great sea, two hundred feet from crest to crest, is running as slick and silent as oil.

A whale "family" is a loose social group of about thirty whales. It is never the same from one month to the next. It is part of a great school consisting of many families. The family of the Little Calf includes young males and young females, pregnant cows, nursing cows with calves, and an old bull who is usually a half-mile to windward from the nursery. The social pattern of this group has long been familiar to whale hunters, who call it a "harem." At the breeding place the adult females outnumber the adult males, and the males are distinctly larger than the females. Both features are typical of polygamous animals. One might think that sperm whales have been forced into this social scheme in order to gain mutual protection in the harsh and boundless sea, except for the fact that some kinds of whales seem to live solitary lives, with no apparent social structure.

One day follows another as the nights grow longer and the morning sea fogs of late summer are swept away by the clear winds of autumn. Through September, in waters from Mexico to the Hawaiian Islands, swollen cows are bringing forth their young; some even in October. Far to the north in the Bering Sea and along the Aleutian Islands, the bachelor males and solitary bulls are feeding. Fat and warm-coated, they are in no hurry to turn southward for the winter. Virgin females have been feeding off British Columbia. They now feel the chill of fall in the currents of the North Pacific Drift and turn slowly toward the tropics. Scattered among them are mothers attended by suckling calves, one year or two years old.

The migrations of the whales, their movements from season to season, their integration with the family at one time and separation at another, their sense of belonging with companions of similar age, sex, and breeding experience, all suggest that a multitude of signals from the world around are constantly reaching their minds through ears, eyes, skin, and doubtless other perceptual channels as yet undiscovered. The life of a whale is surely complex, and by no means as monotonous as one might think. The daily task of living involves far more than rising to breathe, sinking to feed, staring at a liquid plain, and swimming . . . swimming . . . swimming.

In the group of cows straggling southward from Vancouver Island is one who keeps rudely shoving her calf aside, indicating that she has lost all interest in the role of nursing mother. Her calf is now two years old—a great, hulking, twenty-four-footer with a weight of nearly four tons. Of late he has adopted the annoying habit of tearing food from her mouth as she rises from the deep with struggling fishes in her grasp. Earlier she felt the instinctive rightness of sharing her food with her calf; now she feels that it is time for him to shove off for good. Furthermore, she happens to be one of the cows who is on a two-year rather than a four-year breeding cycle; she was bred again when her calf was only four months old. For the past sixteen months she has been nourishing a small life within her body and another one without. No wonder she is weary of motherhood!

As the Little Calf grows daily more aware of his world he is fascinated by the actions of the harem bull (his father, unbeknownst), the great, black, sixty-ton beast who guards the perimeter of the family circle. The bull is often absent for an hour or more on some mysterious errand. Where does he go so quickly in broad daylight on an open sea? Down, down, on a long, slanting course through the zones of green and purple twilight to utter blackness below. Luminescent fishes and strange blobby creatures brush past his undulating tail as he goes steadily deeper. The pressure is now one hundred tons to the square foot; the water is deathly cold and quiet. At a depth of three thousand feet he levels off and begins to search for prey. The sonar device in his great dome is operating at full peak. Within a quarter-hour he reads an attractive series of echoes and he turns quickly to the left, then to the right. Suddenly he smashes into a vague, rubbery, pulsating wall. The acoustic signal indicates the center of the Thing. He swings open his gatelike lower jaw with its sixty teeth, seizes the prey, clamps it securely in his mouth, and shoots for the surface. He has found a half-grown giant squid, thirty feet long, three hundred pounds in weight. The squid writhes in torment and tries to tear at its captor, but its sucking tentacles slide from the smooth, rushing body. When its parrot beak touches the head of the whale it snaps shut and cuts a small clean chunk of black skin and white fibrous tissue. The whale shakes its prey in irritation.

Suddenly the surrounding water fills with light and the bull lies puffing in the sunshine. He crushes the squid's central spark of life, its gray tentacles twist and roll obscenely like dismembered snakes. The Little Calf watches in excitement as the bull begins to breathe in great gasping drafts, expelling each breath in a pyramid of vapor which holds not only stale air and moisture but also a special kind of foam or mucus. Patches of this dry like meringue on the top of his head before he is done with breathing—fifty breaths or more. Now at ease, the bull turns to the dead beast and leisurely chomps it into bite-size pieces, each the size of a football, and thrusts them mechanically into his gullet with muscular tongue.

OCTOBER

O N a morning in early October the sea is glass, without a ripple or sound. A feather falls from the breast of an albatross winging its lonely way northwestward to the Leeward Islands and home. The plume drifts lightly to the sea and comes to rest on a mirror image. It is a day when time itself is still.

At the first glow of dawn the Little Calf and a companion of his own age have filled their bellies with warm milk. Now they are looking for fun. A vague tingling, an unquiet, grows in the water about them. For a while they pass it off as porpoise talk, a part of the daily world, a murmur as common as the lapping of waves. But ever more clearly a pulsating beat comes through the sea. In unison the whales flex their muscular bodies and surge ahead to gain velocity. In a rush they raise their stubby heads above the water and gaze quickly but intently toward the horizon, right and left. (They cannot look straight ahead, for their eyes are on their sides.) A half-mile away they dimly see the flashing bodies of white-sided dolphins at play, bursting the placid sea and scattering a million jewels behind. The dolphins are hot in pursuit of a low-hulled gray ship, a ship flying the Navy jack and moving on a zigzag course at six knots.

The little whales drop heavily into the water and take off at full speed toward the fun. (In later years they will learn to fear the sound of men and ships; now they are young and reckless.)

25

Little Calf

The ship is the *Shark*, a training ship for antisubmarine warfare, carrying recruits who are learning both to echo-locate, or range, and to listen for the sounds of enemy craft ranging in turn for *them*. Below deck a chief and fifteen men are sitting in a darkened room, their faces dimly lit by the green glow of an oscilloscope. A loudspeaker in the ceiling is crackling in a torrent of nonhuman sound. Squeaks, squawks, whistles, hums, and clipping notes are interlaced with the steady "ping-ping-ping" of the ship's transmitter.

"Those are dolphins coming in," says the chief, "and I'll put them on tape for a playback after lunch. I'll run them along with the fish records we picked up outside San Diego." He describes each characteristic sound and its word-picture on the glowing screen. The sounds are not voices; they are vibrations. They are not made by vocal cords and are largely inaudible to the human ear without the aid of instruments—that is to say, they range in shrillness to nearly ten times the upper hearing limit of a sharp-eared human being.

As the small whales close in, the dolphins are at the bow. They are having a wonderful time, though the ship is not zipping along as fast as they would wish. One dolphin takes delight in crowding his companions, one by one, to the clean prow cutting the water, forcing them to flip explosively or else be run down.

The racket of the loudspeaker is unbearable and the chief turns down the volume. From the bridge comes a message that twenty or so dolphins are playing around the ship. (It is hard to count them, for some are running submerged.) "I've got a man at the peak taking movies," says the skipper. When the vessel returns to port, the film will be developed, the species

26

will be identified by the whale expert at the University, and the sound track will be properly labeled as to source. It will eventually be duplicated and sent to sound libraries in Navy installations all over the country.

As the volume dies the chief frowns and holds up his hand for silence. He fiddles with the knobs. Another "ping-ping-ping"—erratic, now loud, now faint, like the distant noise of carpenters shingling a roof or men beating a boiler with hammers—comes in. He shuts off the ship's own pinger and asks a recruit to phone the bridge. Is another ship coming in?

In a moment he has the answer: two small whales are running alongside about a hundred yards off the starboard beam. "They're sperm," the skipper adds, for he has turned with an inquiring glance to the bos'n, an old-timer who once served a hitch on a whale-catcher out of Eureka, California.

"Listen sharp," says the chief to his men. "I've never heard a sperm before, at least for sure, but during the war I had a couple of bad times on a PYC, wondering whether to call for a depth charge. Both times, the sound wasn't quite right for a sub and I sweated it out."

Now coffee circulates in heavy mugs and the wardroom talk turns to the underwater sounds of cetaceans, how the slapping of tail flukes or flippers may resemble a ship's propeller, and how the resonant phonations may simulate the noise of instruments.

"The body origin of whale sound is poorly known," continues the chief. "Sometimes a man in the open air can hear a whale talking and can even see bubbles rising from its mouth or nose. I personally don't think the bubbles have any connection with the source of sound. From what I have read, the sound is like the screech you hear when you partway turn on a kitchen faucet with a leaky gasket. The source is 'cavitation,' or a string of vacuum bubbles in liquid."

A sharp recruit suggests that it might be possible to disguise a submarine as a whale by playing back, underwater, the proper pulse trains. The chief smiles. "Maybe you've got something there. I'll give you another idea about as practical: the ideal hiding place for a sub would be at a depth of two hundred feet, among echoing shoals and rocks, just below a thermocline—a sharp change in water density—and underneath a school of whales. That setup would be guaranteed to fool the smartest man at the listening post."

The chief turns on the *Shark*'s pinger again and the hammering duet of the Little Calf and his companion fades away. The whales, irritated by the unfamiliar staccato ping of the monster they are shadowing, have lost interest. They start back to seek the quiet of the family, which now seems to be a frightful distance away. The small whales have learned a lesson in time and space.

The Little Calf is slowly beginning to recognize and to remember certain members of his group. There is a great-aunt whose lower jaw was horribly twisted and nearly broken off years ago in a fight with a killer whale. The tip of her jaw is bent at an angle of forty-five degrees; it juts outside her mouth, all covered with algae and barnacles. She is not bothered by the deformity but continues to swim actively and to catch fish and squids.

Another old cow has seen forty-three winters. She has escaped the whale hunters because she is often with calf, and the hunters will not shoot a nursing mother. Her back is heavily scarred with pale circles ranging in size from that of a teacup to that of a dinner plate. Some of them are made by the powerful sucking disks that fringe the tentacles and arms of the squid and octopus. Other circular marks are reminders of stinging attacks by lampreys, those wriggling, yard-long, slimy brown creatures that repel even the zoologist. The lamprey way of life is to fasten itself to the body of a whale or a fish by means of round, rubbery, sucking lips. The mouth is lined with rasping teeth which leave permanent marks or, from a small and helpless victim, drain the life blood entirely. On whales, the scars are pure circles, hundreds upon hundreds, strewn thickly at random like overlapping craters of the moon.

(A fisheries officer once wrote me from South Africa, "Who would have put the numerals 39 in white paint on a porpoise?" What he saw was almost certainly a set of curlicue marks made by the teeth of some marine predator.)

A third female in the Little Calf's group was the victim of a weird accident. On her back, above and behind the right flipper, is a long callused ridge. It will stay there until she dies. If she is killed by a whaling crew, the flensing knife of the butcher will dull itself on a hard thing buried in the ridge. The thing is the bony bill of a swordfish, or broadbill. Four years earlier, on a moonless night, she was cruising off the Bonin Islands when she neared a group of swordfish on a collision course. One of them, a big eight-hundred pounder, took evasive action at the same instant she turned. At a speed of thirty knots the long sword slipped cleanly and smoothly into her back, buried itself in the blubber, and snapped off at the base. The entry wound closed in a few weeks and the sword was entombed.

Another member of the group was attacked deliberately,

I think. The evidence for intentional attacks by swordfish goes back to the Second World War when ships carrying bales of rubber were torpedoed in the Mozambique Channel. Many bales drifted ashore. Beachcombers saw that some bales contained the buried tips of spears of marlin and swordfish, as many as four tips to a bale. In one bale there was held firmly a spear tip two feet long, representing a four-hundred-pound marlin, along with the embedded teeth of a great white shark. Poor marlin! He had struggled in vain to withdraw his beak; he was attacked by sharks; and one of the sharks in a frenzy of blood lust had sunk his razor teeth into the bale. The bale carried ashore the mementos of the struggle.

In 1967 a swordfish punctured the hull of a submarine. The mini-sub *Alvin*, cruising off Georgia at a depth of eighteen hundred feet, was rammed so hard that the swordfish could not withdraw its thirty-inch bill. The crew brought the craft to the surface, pried the bill out of the hull, and fried the choicer parts of the fish for dinner.

(Of the swordfish, Oppian of Cilicia in A.D. 180 remarked, as translated, "Nature her bounty to his mouth confined, gave him a sword, but left unarmed his mind.")

Other members of the whale group are less plainly marked, but the Little Calf can identify them also. Each has a scar pattern, skin pigment, and click-voice. All the older whales have been repeatedly scratched and bitten around the face by beaks of giant squids. These horny mouthparts, which can sever a man's finger, leave long white marks on the thin black epidermis of the whales. Covering the background of the skin is often a maze of white lines, straight and curved— graffiti, the tangled tracks of a thousand attacks by rasping beaks and horny teeth and scratching, clawing feet.

30

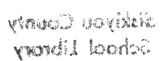

One of the older females has a dent on her forehead from a collision with the sea floor. Traveling at high speed in pursuit of an angler fish, in inky darkness a half-mile down, she grazed a rocky pinnacle.

Another younger female has a skin furrow where a harpoon fired by an apprentice whaler struck the water at a low angle and skipped along her back without exploding.

Still another carries in her backside a rare souvenir: a stainless-steel tube with Russian lettering, a tracer mark implanted by a biologist of the research vessel *Aleut*, out of the Vladivostok Marine Station.

Now a strange female joins the group, a whale newly arrived from the warmer waters of the south. The Little Calf circles her warily. Sprouting from her back and sides are a dozen creatures, sickly gray in color, sixteen inches long—fish, to be sure, but not quite proper fish. One of them falls softly from the body of the whale and swims with feeble strokes toward the Little Calf. On the top of the creature's head there is a long oval pattern of fleshy treads like the sole of a yachting shoe. It is a suction pad—adhesive disk—and the creature is a whale sucker or remora. In the long course of evolution this kind of organism has given up its freedom and part of its muscular strength in exchange for the comfort of hitchhiking on larger animals. Attachment has become a way of life. Without a host upon which to fasten, the remora is doomed, for in the open sea it cannot long escape the rush of its enemies: sharks and barracudas.

The Little Calf darts away and the gray creature sinks, flopping down and deeper down. On the following day, the visitor from the south is nearly rid of her fellow travelers. A week later all are gone; her skin is clean. The water is too cold

31

for their comfort and they have cut loose, to die or to fasten to a southbound host.

On a chill, drizzly day in mid-October the Little Calf sees emerging from the mist a strange craft. This is the *Orchid*, designed by scientists for sea research and photography. She is cruising at her usual speed of seven knots. Suddenly the telegraph signals FULL ASTERN. The vessel shudders; the dishes fly in the galley; the chairs in the saloon bring up with a crash against the fore wall.

Thrashing in the wake of the screw is a smallish, ten-ton female whale. She was dozing peacefully at the surface, barely awash, dead ahead, while the man at the wheel of the *Orchid* stared at a spout off the starboard bow. She is the young female who carries in her backside the stainless-steel marker with the strange device. It will never get back to Vladivostok, for the bearer is mortally injured. She sends out a wild, ragged call of distress and two of her companions move in. They defecate in sympathy. They put their shoulders under her body on either side and try to support her at the surface. Other whales come from all sides, showing the instinctive care-giving behavior of cetaceans that biologists once scoffed at but now accept as real.

In the haunts of the Little Calf, a crew of adventurers on the brigantine *Fairy* are homeward bound from Easter Island to California. The ship moves slowly under sail, her motor stilled. The crew doze, or mend clothes, or polish tackle.

Suddenly a cry breaks from the wheelhouse, half in jest, "Tha-a-a-r she blo-o-o-ws and sparm at that!" There is a swift patter of bare feet on deck, a rush to the bow. The *Fairy* has penetrated to the very center of the Little Calf's group. Whales churn out in all directions, one passing so close to the *Fairy* that the rank smell of its breath drifts to the nostrils of the men on board. Tremaine, the teen-age son of the captain, is hanging over the bowsprit. He cannot contain his excitement. He grabs a shark iron, a keen-edged harpoon with line and float attached, and seconds later hurls it deep into the back of a small female that slides beneath him. Good God!

The whale is no less astounded than the boy. The line speeds from the bucket like a living thing. "Lower away," cries the captain, and the crew drop a motor launch over the side, with the captain at the wheel and Tremaine at his side. As they near the wounded animal, they hesitate. Three large whales have returned to the scene of action and are circling the victim —she is a yearling half-sister of the Little Calf.

The line parts, though whether from a bite or from the sheer impact of a passing body is not at the moment clear. Tremaine quickly fastens a new line to the bight of the old one and the captain succeeds in planting a second iron near the whale's left flank. Bleeding from both wounds, she moves away in a streak of foam, towing the launch behind her.

Meanwhile, the *Fairy* moves in under full power and two sailors carry rifles up to the peak. They blaze away at the running whale for an hour and are about to quit from exhaustion when they see the line go slack. The lifeless body rolls in a pink wash.

They haul her partly out of the sea with the ship's tackle and a line looped round her flukes. When the winch begins to shudder and whine, they stop—she is far too heavy to handle. They take movies; they strip a long, dark-red, ten-pound sirloin steak from her back and cut her loose to the sharks.

On the eastern edge of the feeding grounds of the Little Calf's family, brown seaweeds, torn from their moorings on the continental shelf in a brutal gale of wind and swept to sea, float in a vast circle. Oozy golden stems hang deep and trailing. They sway in concert, slowly turn and twist; the filtered sunlight threads the tangle and loses itself in the greeny gloom below. Here and there a stem holds in its grasp a round stone, and as the plant dies the stone falls unseen to the floor of the sea, far from its native bed. Streaming on the surface, and all in one direction, bright leaves flow in the current. The ocean is pricked with a million glancing lights where fronds catch the breeze and fold back and forth, back and forth. Brown domes, bulbous floats, nod and jerk like puppet heads. Shore fishes, carried along in the vast confusion of the storm, dart through the sapless foliage, exploring, seizing the tiny creatures that rain from the stems.

Into the floating forest come the Little Calf and his family. Though he has often seen kelp he has never seen such a tremendous bed far at sea in the blue-water zone. He probes the tangle, rolls a mouthful of strands, and spits them out. They have a faintly foodlike flavor, but not to his taste. With his little back just below the surface he pushes experimentally into the mass. The stems slither against his skin—not a bad sensation, really. His eyes are useless in the jungle of rippling brown and shade, and his ears pick up a babble of soft echoes. With eyes closed he moves slowly ahead in this new and delightful world. He is driven by a primordial urge to discover, to change pace, to test the environment for possibilities—the

34

urge that powers the motion of evolution. (The motion is often toward a dead end, to be sure.)

When he surfaces after ten minutes he finds that a half-brother has been cruising on a parallel course. Together they rush through the kelp, leaping and twisting, churning the sea into brown foam, trailing streamers behind them, splashing in pure abandon. The fun ends abruptly when the Little Calf rams the broad side of the harem bull and takes a blow from the bull's tail that sends him reeling back to the comfort of his mother. He sneezes loudly, with a flowering of mist.

Gliding eastward through the entrance to the Strait of Juan de Fuca which leads to Puget Sound, a great-uncle of the Little Calf is following a long procession of chum salmon. The fish are moving steadily to the tributaries of the Fraser River, where they will soon leave their shining eggs in the gravel and die. They are the last of the fall run. It has slowly penetrated the mind of the whale that the fish are increasing by the moment. They are funneling into the sweet ribbons of fresh water that intertwine the salt, each fish in its own mysterious way seeking out the bed that gave it life three or four years ago. All this is beyond the ken of the whale. He knows only that where he once picked up an occasional salmon in an hour of chase he is now in a thick flashing of silver shapes—more fish than he can swallow. Sheer chance has led him east. He passes by the trailing lines of fishermen from Neah Bay and Sekiu and Pysht. He is alone. The others of his group are feeding far at sea, in the blue water beyond sight of Cape Flattery. Warned by ancient instinct, they shun the narrow channel of the Strait.

And well they may, for the quiet pleasure sea of Puget

Little Calf

Sound is the year-round home of a pack of killer whales, the largest and swiftest of all the predatory mammals of the sea. At the moment, a group of seventeen searches for prey, led by a nine-ton bull. His splendid pattern is pure black and white; full dress, white tie and tails. As he cuts the surface a bold dorsal fin stands five feet high, like a mast. He and his pack are well known to the yachtsmen who see them cruising and thrill at the sight. The whales take a routine course that carries them north, outside Vancouver Island, then down through Davis Strait and the San Juans. Their food is herring, halibut, hake, and squid on the outside passage; salmon, shark, rock cod, and squid along the inside, with an occasional seal, porpoise, or sea bird for a change of diet. (Their name, "killer," is a man-word; it draws embarrassed attention from the most destructive of all killers, Civilized Man himself.)

The leading killer bull begins to echo-locate on the lone sperm whale and turns his pack toward a meal. Many a time they have torn to bloody bits the little piked whales of the Sound, and once they stopped a great gray whale in a running battle of two full hours in the view of excited campers on the beach. But never have they tackled a sperm, a stranger in their midst. While the killer bull hesitates, a rash member of his pack, teeth bared, darts toward the flank of the sperm.

The sperm outweighs his attacker four to one and is skilled in fighting. He has sparred with rival males of his own kind in the mating season ten years in a row. He waits . . . and waits. Then, at the high strategic moment he twists his body in a fierce curve which brings his tail crashing against the killer. In the next motion he drops his jaw and swings it in a ten-foot slashing cut across the bull's soft underbelly. Between one breath and the next, the fight is over. A flabby, writhing strip of black and white, diffusing scarlet, rolls to the surface, as the killer lies in shock.

The distress cry of the wounded comrade is now uppermost in the mind of the pack; hunger is forgotten. They circle in confusion and one female tries to lift the dying animal. The sperm turns toward the west and the open sea. Not again will he venture within the still waters where his caution warned him *no!*

NOVEMBER

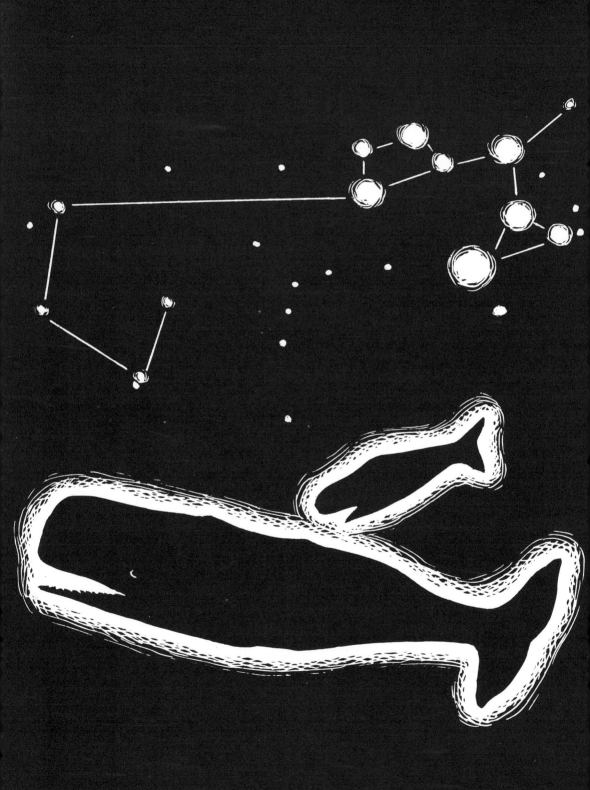

AS the Little Calf tumbles at the surface on the first day of November he sees at the rim of vision a dark speck on the flat of the sea. Too distant for him to identify, it might be the floating stump of a tree . . . the bloated carcass of a seal . . . a wooden crate thrown from the deck of a passing ship . . . perhaps a plastic jug—one of a million jugs, cast-off bits of garbage impervious to water and corrosive salt, jetsam blown by all the winds to the remote beaches of all the seas.

At his next lazy roll the dark blur suddenly grows. The Little Calf is alert. There is danger in the air. His mother changes course and moves away with all deliberate speed, along with others in the group. They breathe in measured tempo, senses sharp and voices low.

In an instant the dark thing is upon them and the family breaks in panic. A heavy, sea going tug, with "LIFE ARENA" blazoned across her bow, approaches in a churn of power. On the low peak there crouches a mysterious metal monster like a pair of giant tongs. A man stands in the crow's nest, muffled in wool against the gray chill of the day. He waves his arm madly and points to the left. Men in yellow slickers run on the after-deck, carrying lines and tackle. The ship turns, heeling in a boil of foam while the men hang to the rigging.

The ship is chasing a small whale, a suckling female born

the year before, another half-sister of the Little Calf. Back and forth the ship pursues her prey like a beagle on track of a hare. Now she pauses while the lookout tries to guess where the whale will blow, now surges ahead with smoke streaming from her stack. The whale tries to catch her sobbing breath but the dark thing is again on her all too soon.

A gunfire blast from the bow—a bright flash—a puff! The monster leaps. The tongs of stainless steel padded with foam rubber clasp firmly round the tapering body of the whale. Another *crack* and a small projectile charge of tranquilizing drug speeds into the flesh of the struggling animal. The ship backs off with a clang of bells. A nylon line stretches taut to the whale, dripping along its length and trembling like a fiddle string.

Now the waiting crew on deck slash the ropes that hold another odd contraption—a great white tub, part boat, part sled, a shallow trough, twenty feet long, of foam rubber reinforced with steel. It splashes to the sea and four men jump aboard, trained for the act. Frantically they pull it into place in front of the tug and directly aft of the whale.

The captain, though he stands in a chill wind, is drenched with sudden sweat. Never before in history have men taken a sperm whale alive. Will he be first? Will the line foul his propellers or break his rudder? Will the whale turn in anger on the sea-sled and smash his men?

He jerks his head and spits a brown quid over the rail, downwind.

The whale is growing quiet. She breathes heavily, with a deep "*Wh-oo-OOF!*" Was the dose of drug too large?

The script for this climactic scene was worked out weeks

before in an atmosphere of endless talk, cigarettes, and coffee. Veterinarians, mechanics, instrument men, biologists, and old-time sailors were all consulted.

The men bring the sea-sled quickly to a point beneath the whale where the black flukes rise awkwardly from the water in the grasp of the metal tongs.

"Make it snappy!" shouts the captain. "I don't like her looks." In life jackets the men leap from the sled into the cold sea. The tug retreats, sliding the whale gently to her bed without a hitch. It is all over.

"By God, we've done it!"

The tug moves slowly astern to keep the nylon line taut. The swimming men hook dangling cables to steel eyes at either end of the sled. The captain signals: "Haul away!" and the great sled with its living load rises from the water. The boom leans perilously over the side; the deck slants; a bucket bangs against the rail. Now a man jerks a slender trip-wire following the line from deck to whale. The tongs spring open, and the whale lies free under the sky, passive, dumb, eyes rolling—a creature pulled against her will into the world of men. She is lowered at last to a cradle on the afterdeck, and a soft girdle of canvas and foam rubber is lashed across her body, pinning her flippers to her chest.

A yellow sun breaks through the overcast. The ship turns north-by-east, three-quarters east, full speed ahead. The radio alerts the owners of Life Arena on the mainland. The sailors change to dry clothing and stand in a quiet circle around the whale, seeing the slowly heaving sides, the tiny buglike creatures moving in confusion on the drying skin, the trembling flipper, the shining eye. Warm-blooded beast and warm-blooded men are translocated in time to a common level—a common stem of life two hundred million years ago.

The cook emerges from the galley, wiping hands on apron, pushing white cap over ear. "Chow's on!" With stony glance he passes the whale. "Whales and porpoises are a sailor's friends," he mutters, as he retreats to the warm comfort of his little kingdom above the fragrant stove. A religious man, in his way.

Now the animal trainer and the veterinarian discuss in worried tones a long red cut across the snout of the whale where she threw herself against a cable. They look at the blisters on her dome.

On through the starry night the ship forges ahead. At break of light the men are out on deck again staring at the whale. She is breathing a little easier, and she lunges now and then against her girdle. The vet smears a white ointment on the blisters. "It's just a sunburn, I think; one hour yesterday was enough to do it!" He rubs an antiseptic cream into the cut. He calls for a man to stand by full time with a cold salt-water spray to keep the tender skin as moist as nature requires.

At two in the afternoon the ship arrives at port; the captive whale is hoisted on a waiting flatbed truck. Reporters from the local press flash their lamps and scribble with thick pencils. An hour later, she is lowered into her final home, a pool of clean, circulating sea water in the aquarium.

The news has traveled quickly; scientists from New York, San Francisco, New Orleans, and Los Angeles are preparing to come and view, at close quarters, a real live sperm whale.

Meanwhile, the worried men of the Life Arena organization try to figure out a food regimen for the little whale. What does a toothless yearling eat? Has she been weaned already?

"At the start," says an old-time keeper, "give her castor oil." Saved from this indignity by the gentler advice of the vet, she is started off on a bland diet. Raw clams, mackerel, cod-liver oil, and vitamins, all blended creamy white and force-fed through a soft tube, are pumped into her stomach.

The formula works. Two gallons go down smoothly on the first try and four on the next. Don't reckon the cost—the whale is showing life. She circles actively, gives all the little signs that seem to say, Okay, all's well.

Three hundred miles away a mother searches for her young. . . .

In mid-November the ocean seldom rests. The black waves hurry southward, ever southward, in the fitful moving cloud shadows of the night. The wind moans softly to itself. To those who love the sea it is a peaceful time, a quiet time. They hear the humming of the universe. When now the music stops, the rolling sea keeps up the beat, the harmony goes on, and in the quiet dawn the sky flames red-grape purple, painted by the dust motes from a volcano's birth ten thousand miles away.

Newcomers, strange to him, are beginning to join the Little Calf's group, the first arriving bulls from the northland. They are in splendid shape; each has put on nearly a ton of pure fat every month during the summer feast among the Aleutian Islands.

At the same time, other bulls are leaving the group and moving south. They are few in number and do not really belong to the group. They live in waters of the southern hemisphere, straying to Mexico only when chance directs their course. In the south it is springtime. Soon the sun will shine there night and day.

The southbound whales are in search of food, the teeming fish life in waters little known to man. The whales move on to Sixty South and still beyond to the edge of broken ice: enormous blocks of white a mile across, palaces, crystal vaults all blue-green, deep with mystery, the water dashing in and out, the moaning of the ice wells, the sudden roll and crash of melting spires. The fragment children of the Great White Continent, the Land of Silence, slide sighing from the mother lode and drift off, to erode, and corrode, and dissolve, and slop away to nothing at all in the Humboldt Current.

(Once I went to the South Pole and beyond, to suck my frozen breath at thirty-five below in midsummer, on the top of the icecap. A vast continent, greater than the whole of Europe and all so clean and quiet—there one can live, for a time at least, on pure emotion.)

The all-surrounding protean world of the Little Calf is filled with a hundred chemicals and a million living sparks and a billion bits of drift, no two alike. It is an endless, moving, thin, transparent soup; a cosmic stock forever old and ever new.

In this pale and swirling broth the Little Calf and his companions play at times with toys that bring them pain. They are forced to glimpse the rougher side of life.

Of late, the Little Calf has tried to snatch remains of fish, the partly chewed debris squirting from the corners of his mother's mouth with each tremendous chomp. This is good, for it teaches him to grasp and tear, to twist and dart and seize

46

the swimmers of the sea. But it is also bad, for now and then a fish is poisonous or bears choking spines or ragged scales. Some fish feed in transit through the deadly "red tides" and hold the poison in their bodies for a while.

A red tide is a living broth of simple cells, neither plant nor animal, but something in between. They contain green organs like a plant, and reddish blobs of pigment, and they propel themselves through the sea by whips as do certain primitive animals. (Must every living thing be plant or animal? It is man that makes the definitions.) These cells are called "dinoflagellates" and they can multiply with amazing rapidity. No one knows why. Among them are species which contain a fearful toxin, perhaps more lethal than botulinus toxin—and perhaps the most lethal toxin on earth.

The stomach of the Little Calf is not yet adjusted to foreign foods, and in his bloodstream the agents of immunity are only slowly building up. The lining of his throat is soft and smooth.

So today he has a bellyache. He slams his anvil head against mother's great side and rubs his corrugated back across her belly. She, source of all blessings, is, somehow, dimly back of all this pain. He thinks he is hungry and he nurses for a while, but spits up the milk in a spasm of distress, a gallon at a time.

The curdled creamy stuff rides in a floating trail behind, while phalaropes in flight break pattern in a quick, ruptive flash of silver and drop daintily to pick the bits.

The mother slides along without concern. This Little Calf is her twelfth (not counting two who never saw the light). She seems to know that their troubles come and go, though probably she does not remember the day some fifty years ago when she herself was playing off the Christmas Reef with a floating ball—in fact a coconut—that brought her grief. She swallowed it in fun and barely got it down. For a week it churned in her lower regions, now stopping the normal flow of food, now letting it by, till nature finally had her way and passed it on.

The mother learned a lesson from her pain. The North Pacific Ocean of today is strewn with nets in which are woven giant balls of green or browny glass, some eighteen inches through. They bear the signatures of shops in China, Korea, Japan, the Soviet Union, Canada, the U.S.A. and Mexico—the homelands of the fishing fleets. The glassy floats break free in storm and circulate to the playgrounds of the whales. Now and then a float disappears into the maw of a whale—but not that of an old whale with watchful eyes.

It is the twentieth of November and the middle of night. A hunter's moon illuminates the world of the Little Calf. The inner pangs of yesterweek are gone and their memory as well. He is content.

The flat molten silver of the sea swells at a point and bursts. Before the Little Calf can grasp the scene, an explosion of shapes appears at the point of rupture. A glistening black monster emerges on his back, thrashing tail at one end and gaping, upturned mouth at the other. In and around his lips, clawing and crawling and dripping, is a loathsome thicket of living limbs. The harem bull is locked in deadly combat with a squid.

Brief moments ago the squid was hunting near the surface, drawn by the light of the moon. He was a moving gray-

48

pink ghost—a vast membrane streaming through a void, a silent flapping of vanes, a soft blur of naked whips. Then suddenly he was a tormented life fleeing in the dark.

The water stills, and the Little Calf slips along at a safe distance of a hundred yards behind the bull. Here nectar lingers in the wake and juicy morsels twist enchantingly to tempt his tongue. Some of them he follows down, and farther down. Now he reaches levels new and strange, where his muscles press and his tendons creak and his guts rumble and he feels for the first time the tingling tenseness of the masters of the deep.

Many miles away by now, among the bulls headed for the antarctic spring, is one who is also diving deep, very, very deep indeed. Chance has brought him to the one place in a thousand where the Ecuadorian cable hangs in a low loop between two submarine peaks, a half-mile down. The first report to reach his consciousness is familiar: Here is a slimy, tenuous, softly resistant thing—a squid no doubt, or food at least. He grasps the thing with lower jaw and gently pulls. It gives, but then with sudden snap it jerks his body round and seizes flipper in fatal coil of steel. He lunges in fright, twists his rubber mass to a shape most unlike a whale and lunges on. A new coil drops around his belly, another around his tail. His lungs flame in agony; sudden stars drift in shoals across his inner vision; a velvet curtain falls. . . .

His is an unrecorded death, for the cable does not break. The soft words flow around his grave; the messages of life and death, the loving words and stupid words, and pesos up and pesos down, and *"cuanto vale mas?"* The luminescent beasts and the dark beasts and the beasts in-between come to rob his tomb and tear the softening bits from his white frame. And the frame, too, unlocks in time, drops to the ocean floor and enters the geologic book, and the pages are closed.

In his first year of life, as well as in the years to come, the Little Calf will see and hear a multitude of ships: the stinking, rackety little troller with one man at the lines; the purse seiner piled high with pungent, kelpy nets; the proud white tuna clipper, queen of the fishing fleet, a million dollars in her frame; the pleasure liner moving south to spice islands, her yellow lights reflecting on the dark pool of the sea, quick laughter from her rail. All these and many other craft the Little Calf will come to know.

But on the last day of November he sees one the like of which he will not see again. The captain of the thing he sees is very sure that once the trip is done, he will never again venture on the open waters of the North Pacific in a vessel of this kind.

The strange vessel is the *Search*, a unique experimental motor ship on her maiden run. A dozen scientists collaborated on her working plans. To a seafaring man she is a monster; a floating workshop crammed with awkward racks for water-sampling bottles, plankton nets and mud-grabs, fishing lines, fathometer, radar, direction-finder, stills and swivels, shackles, pots and pans. When the captain came aboard, he looked around the cluttered deck and rubbed his chin. "Well, I hope the weather holds," he said.

Now the *Search* is two days out of San Francisco with a motley crew. Biologists, physicists, chemists, a deck hand or

50

two, an engineer, a cook, a mate, and Captain Larsen, whose quiet voice and easy smile relieve the tensions mounting in the crew.

On the second night the ship drifts off the Channel Islands under a small sail that holds her steady on the mild sea. The men rig a flood lamp. It hangs from a boom and dips below the surface of the water, spreading a yellow circle of light. The fishery biologist waits with a dip net—a funnel of nylon webbing fastened to a bamboo pole. He knows that darkness can bring strange reversals in the order of life in the sea. Some topside fishes go below, while other fishes, squids, and smaller organisms seek the upper levels. The reasons are obscure, though food must surely play a part, and escape from enemies, too. The water, clear in daylight, is now filled with pale, gauzy particles, some drifting, some jerking along on small invisible tracks, destined to live no more than an hour.

From the black margin of the pool of light a squid comes into view, pumping his jet stream in splendid rhythmic bursts of power, and close behind a great blur of white which suddenly snaps into focus as a California sea lion. As though warmed by the laughter of a crowd and the spotlight of a theater, the handsome beast turns and dives in sensuous loops. The broad flippers flare and fold and curve into art forms molded by the quick pressures of the sea. He folds them at his sides and shoots into the dark, long neck outstretched, a trail of silver bubbles streaming from nose and fur. Back again in the glare he hangs head down, relaxed, limbs weaving idly in the current—a weightless mass. The spotlight catches an eye and flashes back greenish-gold.

The man at the dip net calls in excitement, but the clatter

51

of feet on deck alarms the virtuoso and he disappears. Within minutes, he is a mile away.

The following night the *Search* is far at sea, stopping on the hour to draw a water sample for the drowsy chemist huddled on the boat deck with his back pressed gratefully to the warm funnel from the engine room. Two zoologists play gin in the galley. Lulled at last by the throb of the diesels they stretch out, snoring, on a leather-covered bench. The mindless automatic pilot turns the wheel. The mate smokes thoughtfully on the bridge. The glass is dropping still; it's down to 29; he makes another entry in the log. A storm is coming, that's for sure.

The day breaks calm but the sky is troubled. Across its great vault ribbon streamers run from north to south, all blood-red. The captain reads the log and knows the signs; he orders to turn about for home. Within an hour the wind begins to keen, the rain beats down, the ship begins to rise and plunge.

A young biologist crouches by the lifeboat and hooks his legs around a towing bitt. He holds a telephoto lens, protected by a whipping plastic sheet. A camera fan, he is loving every wild moment. He sees the Little Calf a hundred yards away in a group of six. What a scene for *Life!* The storm is getting under way; far worse is yet to come. The whales are spaced precisely, two and two. They lift together in the swell and he sees the black, flaring nostrils in a quick-shutter scene against the wildness of the dimming light. Each whale is a rolling shadow on the slanting sea, each in a misty, moving frame of white. A rain squall slashes across the frame and shuts it off. The gloom is growing deeper.

Why is my tongue so thick? the young man wonders, and

then he knows. Shoving precious camera under coat he lets the plastic sheet go down the wind and lurches off below, pausing for a wretched moment at the rail. In the dim, smelly cabin he finds the other savants laid in rows. The playing cards and magazines slide on the floor. The sickish fumes of diesel fuel rise from the shaft alley. (Something is loose below.) Damp garments swing in unison from ceiling hooks, dancing to the broken syncopation of gurgle and *thump!* The room turns green on the left as the deadlights plunge beneath the sea, then green on the right, then green on the left. . . .

A thunderous *boom!* The ship hangs in space; the deck tilts sharply; from the vacant lab comes a muffled crash and a cascade of broken glass.

The captain and mate brace their shoulders in a crowded locker and spin a hasty web of canvas and rope: a sea anchor. In a half hour it trails astern and the *Search* finds her head in the storm. She wallows less but plunges more. The rhythm of her engine stays at DEAD SLOW AHEAD. She waits a day and night, and still another day.

Black witches in tattered dress fly past the window of the bridge. Goony birds, perhaps; they are gone before they show.

The Little Calf rises briefly from an underworld of quiet gray to a screaming wilderness of sound and motion—to the slashing fury of a Force Eleven gale. He is hungry, but his mother wants to stay below.

On the *Search* the men toss in their bunks, shivering, though the room is warm. Gray faces flop against gray pillows in the gloom. A voice cries from a troubled dream. A figure rises, leans on a slanting wall, then slowly moves to another cabin. Sweat trickles down the walls in the fetid atmosphere

53

—no one sees or cares. The clock strikes out the watch: BONG BONG!

Another *crash!* There goes the lifeboat through the rail. The vessel trembles. Torrential streams fall from her upper deck, and her lower deck, and now she floats.

The storm loosens its grip as the low blue hills of the Golden Gate begin to loom. They seem to lie forever there; they will not come nearer. Now the death-pale faces begin to quicken. Here's the lee of the Farallons, and then the Gate itself. Everyone is on deck—a babel of talk—the grateful smell of toast and coffee and tomato soup and orange juice. (No onions yet, or frying bacon, if you please.)

So it goes, at times, when men of science try to penetrate the mother ocean, to pry into the lives of whales and seals and plankton; to measure isotopes, and phosphates, and wave dynamics. The ocean plays no favorites.

DECEMBER

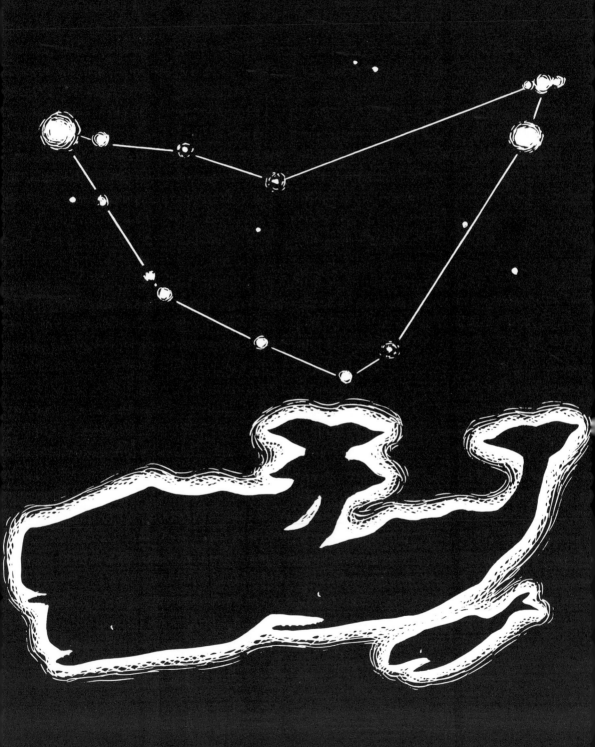

NOW it is December of the year of the whale. An early blizzard whitens the seacoast from Alaska to the border of California and powders the tips of the towering redwoods at Eureka.

A week of violent wind beyond Queen Charlotte Sound drives the Dall porpoises into quiet reaches where they rest awhile and taste the pungent cedar smoke of Indian fires.

The Fur Seal Islands of the Bering Sea are deserted, bare and brown. The dry sea grasses whip against the sand and the red-and-orange lichens burn dimly in the frozen mist. The fur seal pups born this year stream south through the Aleutian passes, uncertain, pioneering, heading south to spend a year at sea. They meet for the first time the challenge of a North Pacific storm. They cannot feed. They cannot sleep. The weaker ones are doomed to die. Their silvery bodies drift by the hundreds to the shore, to wash and tumble in the tides and turn to dirty dishrags in the sand.

Fast ice forms in the Arctic Ocean. It forms along the northern rim of the Bering Sea where the gray whales have been feeding since July. Now they turn with steady purpose to the south, swimming a hundred miles a day. Their goal is Mexico. There, in shallow salt lagoons hidden from human eyes, they will bring forth their young and mate again. The last of their kind, the gray whales were saved in my lifetime by rigid hunting laws. Once a nearly vanished race, their numbers now are swelling. Each year in December when they pass in review below the cliffs of San Diego a hundred thousand people come to watch, and others drift in pleasure launches in their path. Nowhere else in the world are so many whales seen by so many people. No other kind of whale circles each year on so long a migratory route. No other kind of whale comes inland to breed.

Whalebirds, shearwaters, muttonbirds—the same by any name—have deserted the northern passes where they flocked by the millions in September and where they crossed the tide rips and tore the white walls of mist. Now, after a journey of seven thousand miles, they are settled on barren islands off Tasmania and are laying their eggs.

Still feeding along the coast of Mexico, the Little Calf and his family feel the drop in temperature of the current flowing from the east and north. They move by easy stages southward to another stream, a warmer stream. The older whales, cloaked in thick blubber, are not concerned with cold: they are in fact often too warm. The youngsters, though, prefer the milder areas.

During the long impersonal course of evolution those mothers who by chance remained nearest the equator, and yet in pastures rich in food, were most successful in their motherhood. Their young survived. The chance became the habit; the chance assumed "survival value."

In the bodies of the newly adult males, ten years of age or more, new urges start to prick, new itchings flow and ebb (but spring is still three months away). They nose around the female whales, restless and disturbed. Repulsed, they wander

58

off to feed and play. Some travel on . . . and on. . . . They reach Korea and the islands of the Kurile Chain. They pass the junks and sampans—the *skimbo sens*, the small and valiant ships of the Orient. They rub against new fellows of their kind, but yet not kin; their voices somewhat strange; their blood-lines surely similar, but alien.

The mother of the Little Calf is hungry. Too long she has dozed in the winter sun, only inches under the surface of the sea. She sighs. She draws a dozen deep drafts of air and then she turns below. Her tail flashes against the blue. She does not sink, she undulates, she presses firmly down. Her heartbeat drops to ten per minute, barely thumping, slow, pumping five gallons at a stroke. The blood retreats from limbs and skin and tail; it keeps alive the massive brain and heart. The red-black muscles of her flesh begin to pour their hidden stores of oxygen into her veins.

Now the massive beds of fat begin to serve. Their spongy, oily cells relax and offer up their air. The pressure grows. She continues down. Her body goes in debt for oxygen, but not for long. A trillion cells suspend, they tolerate, they hold. For half an hour she feeds and then she pushes to the top to breathe. Her lungs are clean and fresh; their walls are thin. In sweet abandon she sucks the upper air all pure and unpolluted. Her breath is a rustling sound like a surf on a smooth beach—a soft sighing in the music of the wind. It is a sound like no other on the sea. She has fed two thousand feet below and yet survives.

One morning, as the mother of the Little Calf lies at the surface with baby mouthing her breasts, he pulls away. What's wrong with the milk? It has a most unpleasant taste, a flavor not unknown but never quite so strong.

Over the surface of the sea an iridescent purple shimmer, moving from the east, is spreading around the pair. The mother feels it in her mouth and eyes and moves downwind to cleaner surroundings.

Beyond the horizon a ship is pumping out a slop tank, filled partly with oil and partly with rusty water. The smelly broth of pollution will float for many days, until the sunlight turns it into tarry balls and the currents carry the little balls to the beaches and the seas finally pound them into dark grains of gummy sand.

Brown pelicans and boobies settle to the ocean to rest and feed. The oil seeps into their plumage and slowly creeps around their sides as the downy feathers lose their buoyancy. When the birds take off at last and come to land they tremble in the wind; their skin is wet and cold. Dirt from the nesting ground clings to their oily breasts. They try to preen but only spread the mess.

The scene closes on dark, indefinite forms huddled in the drift, feebly moving, death not far away.

In mid-December the group that the Little Calf belongs to has wandered to a feeding ground at Twenty-two North, between the mainland of Mexico and the Islas Revillagigedo. For no special reason they are separated from the other harem group. In a few weeks the groups will join.

The Little Calf and his family linger here through the latter half of December, lazy and content. They have found a place where food is rich, where cold and warm currents meet and bring together a great variety of squids and fishes.

The harem bull has been here often. Now he dives for an hour and a quarter, as long as any sperm whale can hold his breath. Deep down, the white prow of his body is lit by the pale reflection of a noctilucent cloud containing things too small for him to see, each thing a single cell drifting in a self-perpetuating glow of beauty. He rises to the surface at last with three hundred pounds of new food pressing his stomach.

He knows by throbbing feel the peaks and canyons of the submarine mountain ranges; the oozy fans of silt sliding softly, unseen, over the black plains; the awesome cliffs and grottoes; the meandering rivers of brine coursing their ancient channels in the rock. He knows where the octopus hides and where it can be seized when it strays from the safety of its cave. He knows the shape of rotting treasure craft and the rusting hulls of modern ships of war, complete with small, particulate, rusting heaps of metal representing men.

He and the other old-timers of his group have memorized the world below—at a certain cost to their handsome bodies, to be sure. They carry the scars of contact with hidden rocks: teeth chipped and broken, foreheads scarred and furrowed. In the world around them—their biosphere—lies their greatest peril.

We humans here on land tend to think that all wild creatures have important "enemies," in terms of larger, fiercer beasts that feed by habit on them. But what about the lion and the wolf? The grizzly bear? The shark and crocodile? From whom do *they* flee? From none, except while they are young or when they are beset by others of their own kind. Their enemies are the small, erosive, unimpressive costs of living: the storms and droughts, fires and floods, days of starvation, dangerous cliffs and treacherous bogs, thin ice, scratches, infections, tumors, lice and other biting bugs, roundworms and tapeworms, broken teeth and bones, poisonous foods, and all the thousand natural shocks that flesh is heir to. Death comes to them slowly, not as the quick extinction of a rabbit surprised at his nest by a fox. The king of beasts dies with a whimper in the dark thicket. And the great sperm whales die far at sea, their passing rarely known to man.

In late December the Little Calf is beginning to wander more often from his mother's side. He watches with keen interest a group of six-year-olds at play; his older half-brothers. They have found a floating log ten feet long and as thick as a fence post; battered, soft to the touch, and festooned with greenish strands of seaweed. Long ago it tumbled down a Kamchatka river, followed the lazy North Pacific Drift, and is now moving along in waters off California. One of the young males takes the log in his mouth and whips it from side to side, growling in whale language, as if enjoying an imaginary conflict with a fearsome creature of the deep. What fun! What an exquisite feeling in his mouth, where chafing nubbins of teeth are slowly pushing upward to the surface of the gums—they will not reach the surface until he is nine years old.

His fellows see the action and move in on the target. One of them is struck by accident on his tender belly. Anger floods his brain. Transformed in a flash to a fighting bull he wheels away in a churning circle of foam, shoots back like a torpedo, and rams a startled companion. The community click-talk changes its tenor. The young whales, impelled by strange new feelings, arrange themselves like petals on a daisy, heads pointing toward the center, tails flung outward.

Then the wildness passes and again they tug happily at the log, flipping it from side to side.

The Little Calf has now followed his mother and several other whales on a feeding trip to green water within sight of the Mexican coast. The harem bull was not aware of her going, nor would he have stopped her had he known; she is not in heat and therefore not attractive. Mother and calf are now wallowing in the midst of a peculiar stream of marine organisms, a vast, incredible Noah's Ark population of bony fishes, sharks, and squids; sea birds and seals; porpoises and whales. Birds by the thousands, wheeling, screaming, and diving, give evidence that the stream extends beneath the surface of the water for many miles. It is an amazing river of life.

Its smallest units are drifting specks, plants invisible to the naked eye, now multiplied to numbers beyond all reckoning. Two weeks ago, in an eddy current of the southeastern Pacific, the stage was set for their blooming. The environment was suddenly right for a population explosion, as it had not been for several years. The critical factors of protracted sunshine, upwelling of seawater heavy in nutrient chemicals, and drop in temperature combined to trigger the explosion. The animals now composing the stream of life have little in common except that all are gorging on creatures smaller than themselves, down to the microscopic crustaceans in the second link from the bottom who are feeding in myriad pink swarms upon the one-celled plants.

Several hundred sperm whales in migration have paused to enjoy the food riches, while others, including the Little Calf and his mother, have been drawn here from their wintering grounds. For one old bull the feast is a climax to a long life. He is now seventy-five years old and in poor health; he will not live through the winter. Another bull is younger, larger, and in better condition; he has reached his prime at age forty-four and will grow no more. His appetite is insatiable. Though he rests near the surface of the ocean for several hours in midday and feeds mainly at night, he stows away two tons of food every twenty-four hours. Squids and fishes of a dozen kinds go through his maw; he drives ahead blindly. When a bitten chunk of tuna falls from his mouth he swallows the rest and tarries not to retrieve the scrap. A length of fishline with six hooks, wound around the tail of a ten-foot shark, goes down his throat without a hitch. The furrows underneath his throat stretch to accommodate the mouthful, though his stomach pouch (one of four in a row) tries spasmodically and briefly to expel the mass. A young sea lion, far from his home in a rocky cave of Isla Cedros, is sleeping at the surface, glutted near to bursting. He awakens in alarm. His last image of the world is a cavernous whale mouth fringed with white, blurred in a rush of foam.

While the Little Calf is resting with his companions, disaster strikes another group of sperm whales on the strand of Perkins Island, in far-off Tasmania. (There's a saying among biologists that no wild animal ever dies of old age.) Thirty-seven bulls have moved southward from the tropics, forced out by more belligerent males, excluded for one season at least from the joys of harem life. It is summer in the Southern Ocean and the bulls are leading a straggling procession of displaced bachelors and battered old fellows toward the rich pastures of the sub-Antarctic seas. As the bulls turn a rocky headland of Perkins Island on a falling tide, in a brisk onshore wind, they suddenly panic. None has been here before. Strange, confusing echoes return from the reefs, the breakers, and the tide rips. They plunge wildly ahead, following the leader.

A week later a reporter for the *Queensland Witness* stands on the beach in a daze, recording the greatest known disaster of its kind among sperm whales. A thousand tons of black rotting meat are strewn about. Unsupported by water, the lumpish bodies have collapsed; the jaws gape tragically; dark oil oozes into the sand.

"What's your opinion?" the reporter finally asks a sunburned fisherman who has walked from his shack two miles around the point. "Mass suicide?"

"Well, I was pulling my crayfish pots last Tuesday midday and she was blowing pretty hard when I begin to hear this kind of *moaning* or maybe *roaring*. It scared the hell out of me. I've lived here thirty years and never heard nothing like it. It kept on all afternoon and all night. By Wednesday morning it was gone. Jack, here"—pointing to a pal—"come down the coast and told me what it was all about. By then they was all dead. The way I figger it, the bull whales were hot after a cow and they forgot to check the tide."

Perhaps this explanation will serve. Whale scientists, though, will point to the fact that only toothed whales are known to run aground in groups, and only toothed whales depend strongly on echo-location. In unfamiliar, shallow waters, may not these social animals be confused by false echoes and perish in a mad stampede to follow the leader?

JANUARY

THE Little Calf's size is increasing daily. He nuzzles warmly at his mother and sucks. Each full, fat, satisfying meal leaves him replete. A thin plaque of ivory settles on the root of each tooth, a lasting metabolic product of the meal.

But what is he thinking? Is he fearful? What new, exciting images troop across his plastic mind? What new linkages (in neurologic terms) are forming in his brain? Does *color*, for example, strike his memory first, or *form?* Alas, how little we know—how little we can ever know. How little we can penetrate the mind of a creature left so far behind in the evolutionary attempt at a fuller life.

In early January the harem group begins to move north and west, raggedly, on an aimless course, a few miles a day. The Islas Revillagigedo drop below the skyline for another year.

When the Little Calf was born four months ago the family included sixteen cows; now there are fourteen. The mother of the yearling captured for Life Arena searched for her calf until the tension in her breasts eased away. By then she was far from the group. She traveled alone for a month in subtropic waters and joined at last a passing band of whales, largely strange, but including a few known to her from association in the past.

The sixteenth cow disappeared completely from the harem group. Her bloated carcass, a seven-month fetus within it, drifted to a rocky beach near Manzanillo, where the ravens and gulls and wild dogs and skunks feasted on the black meat for many weeks and after the flesh was gone feasted for another week on the blowfly pupae in the sand beneath it. Perhaps her pregnancy was one of the extremely rare type in which the fetus grows outside the womb and finally stops the normal flow of blood and pinches off the mother's life. Who can say? Her bones turned chalky white in the fierce Mexican sun, and once a turtle hunter, a beachcomber, found welcome shelter for the night by throwing his poncho across a pair of her long ribs.

On the twelfth of January the Little Calf's family overtakes a large group of sperm whales, two hundred or more. These are not unexpected, for they have been leaving a broad and well-marked trail of sensory clues: muffled smashing noises, low-pitched groans, clicks, and the creakings of rusty hinges—the fugue and plainsong of a wandering band, as well as clues that can be tasted: urine, pale diffusing clouds of yellow feces, and floating lumps of ambergris, a most peculiar body stuff.

Ambergris, a gray, waxy substance, grows in the large intestine of sperm whales and in no other species. Boulders of it up to nine hundred pounds in weight float on the sea. Its pungent, earthy odor is deceptive, for when purified in the laboratory it is transmuted to a perfume base worth ten dollars an ounce. "It always reminds me," says Christopher Ash, in *Whaler's Eye*, "of a cool English wood in spring, and the scent when you tear up the moss to uncover the dark soil underneath."

In the trail of the whales are also visual clues to their passing: birds wheeling and diving to snatch at fragments of food,

and sharks following to scavenge. These camp followers remain for a day or so and then wander off, while others take
their places. A great white shark, thirty feet long, follows the
group with interest for a week, but no crippled whales fall behind; the fearsome eater finally turns away. The whales pass a
basking shark, the largest of all the fishes of temperate seas,
forty-two feet in length. In spite of its sleepy name, it swims
steadily near the surface with open mouth and goggle eyes,
feeding and breathing in one efficient motion. Plankton
masses cling in reddish gobs to its gill rakers until they finally
pass deeper into its throat and disappear.

When the Little Calf is hungry he follows his mother's
flank, no more than inches from her finely sculptured form.
The great creation and the small creation move in silence as a
double whale. A large swirl on the surface of the water cuts a
smaller one; they both dissolve in an eddy of liquid lace and
suddenly are gone. Low, bushy, vapor-columns linger in the
air . . . then only sky and sea remain.

On the afternoon of the fifteenth of January the Little Calf
is witness to a frightful scene: a full-scale battle between bulls.
Though he will see the pattern repeated many times and will
in fact participate when he matures, this is his first sight of the
great beasts rolling and thundering in his path. The other
whales of the family, the noncombatants, are disturbed by the
sight and sound, for this is the first such encounter of the year.
(The peak of the mating season is still a full three months
away.) The old cows snort explosively. The young cows and
the young bulls hover near the surface at the start of the struggle, trembling like sheep.

Little Calf

A young bull, fifteen years old, has been traveling with the group for several months. He has cut loose from a bachelor group—a timid group of young males coursing the road of the larger herd but a mile or so behind. During the past week he has fed in desultory fashion, coming often to the surface to cruise among the members of the harem group, cutting in and out among the females for hours on end. In passing, he has sparred briefly with other young males and has driven them away with the fierceness of his rushes. Yesterday he found himself near the forefront of the migrating band. In a sudden, blind instinctive surge he slammed his body against a full-grown bull. Incredibly, the bull gave way. The younger whale did not press his advantage but swam on. The impulse to fight was canceled by the quick submission of the foe.

Now in early afternoon of a bright, electric winter day he swims toward the father of the Little Calf who is outriding the harem two hundred yards to windward. A tension, a vast irritation, powers his muscular strokes. Nearing the great bull he rotates his flippers and bends his tail flukes upward. His snout rises from the surface on a long slant, until his eyes are clear of the surface.

The older bull has known for a full minute what was in store. The strong, familiar rasping signals of challenge assail his ears. Annoyed at first, he is now aroused. He reacts by rote to the threat. His broad tail, fourteen feet across, gleams in the sky as he dives to a depth of two hundred feet. He turns and shoots straight to the surface. His snout rises like a black barrel into the air, higher and higher still, until his dome is fifteen feet above the water. Here he hangs, with eyes peering into the open air, circling slowly, while his tail and flippers beat the water in strong sculling motions.

72

The young whale turns on his left side and charges, clapping his jaw violently, forcing each tooth with a smash into the firm white socket of the upper gum. The old bull turns deliberately on his back, belly up, responding in kind with a racket that carries through the sea for a league in all directions. His great jaw swings at right angles to his body, tip waving in air. The first impact of the bodies with a total mass of a hundred tons throws a geyser of green water high into the sky. Within seconds the movements of the whales are lost in a smother of foam. Each infuriated beast is trying to engage the other's jaw, or to seize a flipper—the action is all confused.

The pair sink into a maelstrom. They break apart and race in opposite directions. The tortured surface of the sea tosses like a riptide in a rocky channel.

They turn. They charge at full speed and collide in another mighty, tumbling interchange of power. Now the old bull is riding the back of the younger. His head is out of the water for twenty seconds—a black head marked with red blood and white furrows of blubber. Strangled, bellowing noises from nostrils and throats rise from the vortex of battle.

The third exhausting round is the last. The thrashing beasts, insensate, driven by will, not muscle, tumble into the path of the migrating herd. The other whales speed away in fright.

The jaw of the old bull is locked firmly with the jaw of the young one as the two bodies sink trembling below the surface of the sea in a final contest of power.

Suddenly the young male is done. Silent and dazed; he makes no further challenge, though the old bull tears and worries at his quiet form. The body of the young male is strangely

73

awkward, oddly out of balance, as he swims away. One side of his jaw is broken; it will heal in time. Three ribs are fractured, too. As the blood drains cleanly from the bodies of the whales in the purifying sea, white scars in even, rakelike rows loom on the black skin.

The young male rallies at last and sinks horizontally, deeply, into the ocean, without lifting his tail. He swims a mile before he rises painfully to the surface and takes a solitary position at the rear of the herd. Long, slinky shadows circle his body for a while and then fade away. Blue sharks, attracted by blood, are frightened by the movement of his flippers.

In the confusion of battle, the Little Calf has followed his mother, or so he thinks. She is all at once strange. This is another whale! He starts in panic to search among the herd, all senses alert. But mother has gone below on a feeding trip, and not until the soft colors of evening have painted air and water alike is she reunited with her calf.

The harem bull keeps pace with the herd, though he suffers. Pain jerks at the base of his jaw. A throbbing fever sets in and dulls his senses for a week. He cannot lick his wounds. Held in the rubbery bindings of his own gigantic skin he is a victim of geologic time. He has learned nothing from the battle, nothing at all. He played his part faithfully, and according to the numbers, guided by an invisible coach.

Out where the sea birds wheel in endless circles, patient and watchful, held aloft by unseen strands, the mother of the Little Calf is dozing. She is resting head down at the surface after a rich, bursting feast of albacore, a kind of tuna. It is early morning.

Around midnight last, when darkness was deep and the black sea was dancing with the reflections of a million crystal stars, she saw the glow of something new on the horizon. She turned toward it. Soon she was in a dull fire of light shining from the water and reflecting from the low mist above. The air was quick with light.

She saw the first fish speeding in a school of thousands, each one breaking the dark of the sea in a phosphorescent streak. For a yard or more ahead the shock wave of each fish's body excited the bright particles of the sea, while behind, in the wake, the play of purple and green was an abstract painting of incredible beauty. Amid a wash of color, she set off in pursuit of the nearest fish . . . and then the next . . . and the next. She swam at top speed, throwing her forebody right or left, up or down, as she neared each victim. Most of the fish darted away to safety. At the instant when one loomed at the portal of her jaws, it would whip its silver-and-steel body like a saber and shoot off into the dark. In three hours of steady, exhilarating chase she seized and swallowed two dozen fish, the largest thirty pounds in weight.

The white flesh of the albacore is sweet, rich, and fat. The mother of the Little Calf was suddenly aware that her appetite had overshot her need. She was full and exhausted. So now she is resting while the sun rises slowly in the white mist.

Another cow in the harem is also resting nearby with a stomach full of albacore. Within her tired body she begins to feel a new sensation, something more than fatigue. It is a lowdown thumping, not unpleasant, new but strangely old. A fetus in her womb is starting to make the first swimming motions in the amniotic fluid. During the previous night, while she pushed her great body in excitement to the limit of its power, a subtle message poured into her bloodstream and traveled to the placenta. It percolated through the barrier cells and entered the independent bloodstream of the new life.

The fetus has entered its ninth month of life. About the size of a full-grown man, it is still only halfway through its dark career. At this stage it would be recognizable as a female and is clearly a sperm whale in miniature, though it carries the lingering marks of other ancestors of related kinds. Its little body, once rosy-colored, is turning gray above and whitish underneath. The five fingertips can still be counted. Soon they will merge in the broad outline of the flipper. The ear spot is rimmed by a roundish hump—the fading vestige of a larger ear. The clitoris is sinking into a long groove, no more than a slit, which will later be flanked by nipples (thus · | ·). The eyes are nearly shut; the rubbery jaw twitches from time to time as the fetus swallows a salty fluid which passes through its loins and returns to the womb within an hour.

The baby teeth are all there in rows, but deeply buried, pulpy soft and pink. They are the only set the little whale will ever have. For seven years after she is weaned, until the white cylinders erupt at last from the gums, she will grasp her food with the help of toothless jaws and agile tongue alone.

One set of teeth, and these not fully formed until the whale is breeding. Why? For modern whales, the tooth arrangement satisfies the need. The jaws grow slowly, while the tooth buds keep pace in the deeper tissues. About the time the jaws are grown the teeth have reached their permanent stations. Such an arrangement is reasonable for a beast that lives to a large extent on soft-bodied prey and that swallows many of the prey animals in a gulp, entire. A land mammal, such as a dog, bites and tears its food even before it is fully weaned, and so it needs a set of teeth in early life. If these teeth were to remain in the growing jaw they would soon be standing far apart, useless for the task of chewing flesh. So they fall out in orderly fashion and the permanent teeth erupt in jaws that are then as large as they ever will be.

In the family of the Little Calf there is also an old female who is at the moment neither pregnant nor giving milk, a rare condition indeed for a full-grown female whale. Her last pregnancy was a tragedy, one that occurs once out of two hundred whale pregnancies. She carried twins. She carried them for fourteen months, then brought them forth prematurely and dead. Still, she could never have nursed them both to the age of independence.

Every whale everywhere moves in a sea of total sound. From the moment of its birth until its final hour, day and night, it hears the endless orchestra of life around its massive frame. Silence is an unknown thing. The snapping and crackling of tiny shrimps and crablike organisms, the grunting and grating, puffing and booming, of a hundred fishes, the eerie whining and squealing of dolphins, the sad voices of sea birds overhead, the chatter of its own companions, the undertone of moving water and the drone of wind, all these notes and many more come flooding through its senses all the time. It *feels* the music, too, for water presses firmly on its frame—a smooth continuous sounding board.

The Little Calf is slow to learn the meaning of the various

sounds. In fact, he never learns them all, but only those that have to do with food and mother, danger, something near and something far, echoes from a floating log, the voices of his friends—the ordinary sounds. As a blind man living in the forest comes to know the birds by their songs, the Little Calf comes to recognize the whales that cross his path. Some vibrations are vaguely familiar from the first. These are the voices of the toothed whales, the ancient order of his kind. But the vibrations of the baleen whales are coarse and rasping, meaningless. Often in his baby life he hears a sort of barnyard chorus at a distance, weird and unfamiliar, unforgettable. It creaks and cries, barks, groans, and whoops. He never learns its source.

Today he hears another sound like an interstellar cry. It starts as an eerie moan without dimension, formless. It rises to a scream and then fades away, trembling, descending, echoing faintly, leaving the Little Calf frozen. From whence the cry? It never comes again. Perhaps a creature from the deeps as yet unknown to man? Perhaps an ordinary animal, far beyond its normal haunts? Perhaps a silent creature forced to break its silence by some agonizing pain?

FEBRUARY

WHILE sperm whales by the thousands and tens of thousands are feeding in the temperate waters of the North Pacific, a few hundred old bulls are plying back and forth in the near-freezing waters of the higher latitudes where the currents of the Bering Sea mingle with those of the Pacific. These older males, some of whom have traveled at times with the Little Calf's family, are a motley group of immigrants from many seas. Some were born among the scented breezes of the Caroline Islands, some among the Marshalls, and others among the Gilberts, though most were born in the wide, free ocean far from the boundaries of any sovereign state. Their feeding range in the north is vaguely defined. It stretches in a ragged arc two thousand miles across, from Kodiak on the east to the Commander Islands on the west, all of it lying south of the dangerous eddies that carry floating ice from the Pole.

The bulls rise and fall on the never-ending swells of the open sea. The winter days are short and gloomy now, interrupted by williwaws—violent gusts that spring from the empty valleys of the Aleutians and rip in screaming fury across the sea. The moving wind and the moving waves blend in a flowing sheet of smoke for an hour or so, and then the wind drops away as quickly as it came. Through sleet and snow, through great soft, rolling, dripping mountains of fog, through nights so black they define the word, the whales pursue their prey. They never pause. They do not need to rest; in fact, the steady play of their muscles warms their blood in the icy seas.

They wander through the wide passes of the Aleutians into the Bering Sea, but they stay clear of the narrow straits where the currents are treacherous, and where the tides from north and south meet in contests of strength that bulge the sea into frightful, hissing walls of green as high as the deck of a ship. Here the tide sucks away all at once in a change of direction that lays bare the ugly, ragged rocks which rarely see the light of day.

Now and then the clouds are torn apart by a clean wind, and low in the north a moon rainbow stands quickly against the black sky. Its colors are all in proper order, but soft and uncertain, diluted by the blue reflections of the night.

The whales' passage to and fro may take them in sight of the islands of the Aleutian Chain, the cleanest and fairest of all islands. Volcanic by birth, their pure white cones rise above nine thousand feet, with slumbering inner fires, and puffs of smoke and flame, and cinder fields patterned among the eternal snows. They are sharp and clean, treeless and windswept, the home of foxes and birds.

The yellow-eyed fox picks his way daintily along the shores in winter, turning over stones to lick the sand fleas or to nose among the kelpy drifts for stranded fish and the carcasses of gulls. No fragment, however tattered, grimy, or stinking, repels the little fox in winter. His stomach is taut; anything resembling flesh is food. If he is lucky there will come to his island a great winter tide bearing the carcass of a whale. The fox and his companions will eat their way through the hull of the stranded beast and will revel and wallow for weeks in the oily putrescence. They will beat a well-worn track to and from it on the sand. Their silvery fur will become matted and dark with oil. They will be scarecrows until nature provides them with a new coat in autumn.

From a distance, the islands are all white, but closer they show patterns of brown and gray—beautiful patterns of rank grass and stark stalks of Heracleum and raw clean boulders and whipping stems of the plants that live in the cold, wet air of the northland.

The red-faced cormorants drop in heavy-bodied flight from the cliffs and settle to the sea, jerking their heads from side to side, puzzled at the world around them. The tiny precious, whiskered auklets drift through the mist and settle beside the whales. These birds number in the whole world only two thousand or so—a hundred pounds?—a little band, a fragment species. Tufted puffins—the comic sea parrots—ride out the sea storms of winter in the Aleutians. These world-ranging pelagic birds burrow in the ground in summer. They lay their eggs in secret tunnels. In winter they seek the rolling life of the sea.

Other birds in the world of the whales are ghostly creatures of the night: the fork-tailed petrels. The size of swallows, they flutter and twist in blackness above the sea. They dip, and dip again, for tiny, luminescent plankton life and rise, fluttering.

On the fourth of February, three of the sperm-whale bulls are feeding on smelt-like silvery capelin, in Kronotsky Bay off Kamchatka. Though the fish are small, only six or eight inches long, they are sweet and tender, and their bright sides flash by the thousands in massive, slowly moving shoals.

Off to the westward in the overcast the whales see a pale

suffusion that means the presence of floating ice. It reflects against the gray ceiling. By this and other signs they sense the western limit of their feeding range. They slowly turn about, toward America.

The quiet of the winter afternoon is punctuated by the soft sighs of a dozen porpoises, feeding on capelin too. They are right-whale dolphins, so called because, like right whales, they have no dorsal fin. These sleek black-and-white companions of the whales are moving slowly, surfeited with food.

The grizzled face of a bull fur seal breaks the surface. He grasps a capelin firmly in his teeth and shakes his head in a quick blur of motion to snap the living body of the fish into bits that he can swallow. (He has no paws to hold them.) Drops of spray scatter in a circle around his head. A gull swoops to snatch a silver tidbit here and there. Like the bull whales, the bull seal has chosen to winter in the north at the edge of drifting ice. His summer home is a rocky island off Sakhalin, in the Sea of Okhotsk. For days at a time now in winter he is alone, without communion with others of his kind.

In the sea beneath a dark cliff on the south side of Amukta Island an Alaska cod is grazing through a slimy forest of Alaria stalks. It moves at random among the brown plants at a depth of twenty fathoms. It seizes here and there a crab or a snail, a starfish or a sea urchin. Its three-foot, putty-colored body is all goggle eyes and mouth, and a trembling whisker hangs from its chin. Through the dim light the cod sees a moving figure outlined in silvery bubbles. The cod darts forward and clamps the thing in a set of needle-sharp teeth. The prey is a cormorant, a bird that dives deeply to feed on squids and small fishes (including the young of the cod). Back and forth the fish and the bird wrestle among the weeds, but the cod is in its own element and it swims away with the neck, head, and tapering bill of the bird in its throat.

That night the cod swims into the pass between the islands of Amukta and Yunaska. Around eleven o'clock, a sperm whale cruising through the pass swallows the cod without a pause. Now the life circle is nearly complete. The cod that ate the bird that ate the cod that ate the copepod that ate the diatom will soon enter the bloodstream of the whale; bones and scales and feathers will pass out with the feces, to be attacked by molds and bacteria and broken down into chemicals which will fertilize the growth of new diatoms.

As the sperm whales turn eastward they hear a faint throbbing *whap-whap-whap*, a sound remote from any they have heard before. By instinct they dive, for a thing strange is a thing dangerous. In a few minutes they feel the vibrations more and more compelling. One of them rises for a breath of air. His blowhole begins to gape like a black wet funnel when he hears a sharp *bang* and feels a thump in the middle of his back. The air and water are filled with a tremendous WHAP-WHAP-WHAP! The first shock gives way to a small, stinging pain. The whale blows like a locomotive running wild and dives without waiting to ventilate his lungs.

Thirty feet above, a helicopter is climbing swift and straight into the sky. It is fluorescent orange with its name in black letters—the Russian equivalent of *Star Third*. Long cylindrical pontoons stretch beneath it. Its whirling blades hurl a blast of air against the sea and build a circle of concentric ripples, mingled with the swirl of the departing whale. A bright face peers from a window. The face of a girl?

Little Calf

The *Star* is a "chopper" under contract to the big Soviet research station at Petropavlovsk, where problems of the sea and its fisheries are studied through the year. Last summer, Ludmila Grekova, a girl of twenty-two who is a member of the staff, conceived the idea that whales could be tagged for research more easily by approaching them in a helicopter than by chasing them in a ship. Her idea moved slowly at first in the turgid channels of administration until it reached the office of a young man who was impressed both with the idea and with the sparkle in the girl's gray eyes. An order went to the tool shop and another to the planning room.

So now on the fourth of February a 12-gauge shotgun, pointing down from a helicopter window, has fired a stainless-steel cylinder into the fat back of the whale. The chopper with its pilot and two passengers, one of them Ludmila, moves on in search of other experimental targets. Before the pilot warns that the point-of-no-return is only minutes away, they strike two other whales and a "possible." On the last attempt, the aircraft lurches as the trigger is pulled, and the projectile strikes the side of the whale at an angle. (The marker, if indeed it penetrated, is hidden in a smother of foam.)

The first bull hit is now fifty miles to the east, swimming at full speed on a straight course, trying to shake loose the burning object fastened in its back. Within a week, the entry wound will cease to drain, and in another week the pain will be gone. Next summer, the bull will be taken by the crew of a Japanese whaling boat and the bright marker will be found at the bottom of a cooker by a filthy workman shoveling out the gurry. The biologist on board will shrug his shoulders in annoyance and protest again to the captain: "Why can't the flensers keep their eyes open? Why can't they watch for these markers?" Though he has recovered a marker, to be sure, he doesn't know which whale in the day's catch it came from, though probably it was the big old bull that brought ninety barrels of oil and was surely fifty years of age.

The second bull hit by a marker will carry Tag no. 559 for four years and three months. He will be killed by a gunner of the *Zelenogradsk* en route to the Antarctic whaling grounds and he will be famous, briefly, as the first sperm whale known surely to have crossed the equator. His fate will overtake him north of Guadalcanal, four thousand miles from Kronotsky Bay. He will have traveled a thousand miles a year, though no man will ever know the shape of his track, and the times when he rested, and the times when he forged ahead.

As the helicopter nears the shore of Kamchatka toward sunset, Ludmila scribbles quick notes in her record book, setting down the important events of the afternoon while they're still fresh in mind.

Her companion biologist, Yuri Sokolov, has taken a keen interest in the chase of the whales but he hasn't been able to try *his* device, a gadget which he hopes will help to describe the devious track of a moving whale. (Nothing like it has worked before.) It is a device of wires, batteries embedded in wax, a projectile point.

As the chopper enters Kronotsky Bay, Yuri sees a target: a group of little piked whales, the small baleen whales that frequent the sheltered waters of the coast. He motions to the pilot, telling him by hand signals to carry out the plan they agreed on before they left the base. The chopper dips her nose and points her white pontoons toward the target. Yuri loosens his seat belt with a quick tremor of fear and kneels at the open window, harpoon-gun in his lap. The airstream tears the goggles from his face and draws the tears from his eyes. He is dead on target; he pulls the trigger. *Vr-oom!* A heavy charge of black powder, slow-burning but packed with energy, hurls a two-pound projectile into the rump of the whale, slightly abaft the dorsal fin. The missile travels too fast for his eye to follow it. It is a neat, shiny cylinder packed with printed circuits, transistors, miniaturized organs that, according to plan, will function perfectly. The pole antenna snaps out on schedule and trails behind as the whale doubles its rippling body in naked fright and sounds to the depths where it has always found escape from danger.

Yuri turns to a receiver strapped on the floor of the aircraft and puts on earphones. He listens intently for the mechanical purr which the device has given on command in the sheltered laboratory where it was conceived. He listens . . . whale and ocean are still; no whisper from the faultless cylinder so carefully designed by man returns his scientific love.

On the tenth of February a fishing boat called the *Halcón* is cruising in the subtropical Pacific, along the coast of Mexico, at the southern limit of the range of the Little Calf's family. She is on a trial voyage, a strange voyage, testing whether a purse seiner can be adapted for catching whales. She is registered in a Central American state which is not a member of the International Whaling Commission and whose citizens are not bound by any laws respecting the capture of whales.

Before the voyage the owners of the *Halcón* had a discussion.

"Here we have a fine boat in use for only eight months of the year, when the sardinas are here. Why can't we run her also in the spring, as a whale-catcher? We see the big fellows out there where we spread our nets."

"But whales are frightened by the sound of a diesel. They are hunted only by steamers or sailing boats or pulling boats."

"Is that true, amigo? How does one know?"

The discussion was led by a Portuguese called Beppo, who had worked with a California shore-whaling company. His dark eyes glistened as he described the excitement of the chase and the mountains of red meat brought to the dock to be sold for dog food to make the owners rich.

So at the end of the fishing season the *Halcón* is fitted out with a new set of tackle. There is much scratching of heads: Who knows how to shoot a whale? How big a line we need to hold him?

Finally a cannon is mounted on the peak and a Norwegian named Axel Swanson is hired to shoot it.

The owners find Swanson in a waterfront cafe. He is known to all the fishermen as an ex-whaler from the Southern Ocean, and as a teller of tales to whom one listens politely, and for whom one buys a drink now and then for the sheer poetry of his words. So long in the Antarctic he endured the bitter winds and frozen spray that he now chooses to bask in the tropical sun until he dies. Axel has seen better days. He swears that he owns the best eyes for whales in the whole world, and it is no secret that he keeps them sharp by drinking a great can of seawater each morning as he staggers from his bunk. He dips it from the local pier, and it contains other things than seawater, foreign bits that may in truth keep him healthy by preserving his immunity against everything that creeps and crawls. But along toward noon when the sharp eyes of the great hunter are twitching in the white sunlight, the purifying effects of the oceanic brew have drained away and the grip of *vino tinto* is supreme.

As she leaves on her maiden voyage for whales the *Halcón* is showered with laughter and cheers from the dock, with words rude but basically encouraging. She turns west by south. Where will the first target be sighted?

Three hours and thirty miles later, Pedro, in the crow's nest, sees the sperm whales. They are undisturbed for they have never been chased in these waters. Pedro begins to shout and point: "Ballena-ballena-ballena!"—all one word. He jumps up and down in the barrel without thought for safety.

Axel drops the rope he is splicing and runs to the peak. He rips the canvas cover from the gun, throws off the safety catch, drops the sun-glare goggles from his graying forelock, and swivels the barrel back and forth in a testing motion on its well-oiled track. Though his eyes are bleary his mind is clear. He is again a man of action. He is again the number one gunner among all the gunners of the southern ice. The captain steps outside the wheelhouse to the controls on the bridge where he can follow the directions of Pedro, silhouetted against the sky. Pedro wears a black stocking cap with a red tassel which flies up and down as he jumps. With his red cheeks framed in black beard he is straight from Mother Goose. Twenty minutes later the ship is overtaking the whales and now Axel himself can see the white mushrooms of vapor—three of them, or maybe four. He shouts to the skipper that he wants to give the sailing orders now, but Spanish has left him suddenly and his words are

pure waterfront Norwegian. Fortunately the skipper can see
the trailing wakes of the whales. With a fisherman's quick un-
derstanding of life in the sea he soon is predicting where the
next whale will rise to blow.

Choo-oof! A frightened whale lifts in a majestic black arc
only sixty feet ahead of the ship and the gunner turns his cannon to the spot. He struggles to lower the sight to the back of
the whale but the goddam thing won't lower. The barrel
strikes the teakwood rail. The men had never thought, when
they mounted the gun, that it would be aimed at a target so
near and so low. The whale sounds. Axel rips off a pattern of
oaths and sucks at torn fingernails and drops to a hatch cover,
shaking uncontrollably. The whale escapes.

Since the afternoon is calm and the sea is flat, the *Halcón*
heaves to, twenty miles offshore. She rolls gently on the
groundswell while two of her men attack the forward rail with
chisels and saws. They clear a wide arc so the gun can be lowered another ten degrees. The February dusk falls quickly.
They finish the job by yellow lamplight.

From the dark coastline a soft night breeze springs out and
carries the fragrance of mahogany to the men of the *Halcón.*
They crowd the galley for coffee and chunks of bread and fried
prawns. Beppo is vindicated; he smiles broadly. A whale *can*
in fact be run down by a noisy diesel ship. Tomorrow we will
go after them again. This is more fun than we thought. But
Jesús, they're big fellows! Will the tackle we got hold them?

A drowsy watchman is left on deck, for the ship might
drift ashore if the wind were to change in the night. He
watches with affection as a dozen petrels land on the rigging
near the riding light. He knows them from childhood; they are

called the *aves de San Pedro* because they walk on the sea. They sway on the ropes. Some are distressed by the new motion and disgorge the salmon-colored, oily contents of their throats, complaining softly all the while.

Axel has slipped off his boots. He lies on his bunk, nearly hidden in a blue cloud of tobacco smoke. He badly wants a drink but he knows there is nothing aboard, and in fact there is never any liquor aboard a fishing vessel worthy of the name.

Sharply after dawn the *Halcón* resumes her search for whales. On and on she drives over a fresh green sea. The call for breakfast comes: papayas, tortillas, fried fish, and black coffee. At eight o'clock the welcome shout again comes from the masthead: "Ballena!" Again Axel throws off his gloves, and spits, and fingers the trigger with fanatic eye. His legs are braced widely on the deck. No more than minutes ahead, the great dome of the whale shines before the ship's prow and the life of Axel is resurrected in a teeth-jarring BAM! An acrid cloud of smoke drifts to the bridge. A heavy line lies in the air like a magic wand.

The second explosion is deep and awful. The bomb in the head of the harpoon bursts in the back of the whale. Axel turns toward the bridge and raises two fingers, the sign of victory. He is at the peak of life, the very summit indeed. Any event and any thought beyond will be measured in terms of this moment.

Mercifully, the bomb explodes deep in the muscles a yard above the throbbing heart. At once, the breath of the whale is a pinkish froth and in five minutes her head lowers in the swell. The *Halcón* moves alongside and a man wearing faded pants and rope sandals leaps to the slippery back of the victim, holding a hose. It is an air hose with a sharp steel nozzle which he jabs deep into her flesh. At a signal, the skipper turns a valve and the whale's black body begins to bloat and rise in the water. When she rolls belly up the hose is withdrawn and the inflated shape is tied to the ship and towed toward land, fifty miles away.

Now the *Halcón* is slowed to four knots by her burden. The clock strikes midnight as she rounds the breakwater and enters the small harbor where she will dispose of her catch. She heads for the rendering plant. Here in the fishing season many thousands of tons of sardines and anchovies are cooked in great pressure pots. The hot stew is squeezed through a corkscrew vise. Yellow oil runs out in one direction and out the other rich, redolent brown meal tumbles onto an endless belt running to the sacking room.

When the run of fish is over, the plant shuts down, all but one cooker and one extractor. Here a few of the workers are kept busy processing sharks, rays, and other rough fish, and an odd porpoise now and then.

The manager is waiting on the dock to see the whale. (A hundred men and boys and forty dogs are also waiting to see the whale.) The manager wouldn't bet five centavos on the *Halcón*'s chances, but here she comes proudly round the bend with the dark body lashed to her side and all her deck lights burning. She ties up to the dock to wait for daylight.

In the cool of morning the workmen loop a chain around the tail of the beast and winch her up a slippery platform that leads from the water to the butchering deck. When they pierce her belly with a long knife, such a rush of rank, sulfurous gas bursts forth that the white paintwork on the near side

93

of the *Halcón* is colored a pale smoky brown and her men must scrub it off next day. The flesh of the whale is smoking hot, though she has lain for a day in the cool sea. A workman loops a steel cable around the jaw between her teeth and signals with his glove: *Arriba.* The jaw moves slowly out in agonizing creak and popping flesh. When the strain is final, the cable stops and a man leaps to the slippery head and dislocates the skull.

The rest of the story of blood and lymph would interest only a butcher, except for one fact. When the belly of the whale is slit open and a man puts a hook on the guts to free them from the carcass, the manager is astounded at their massive size. He is a man of curiosity, one of those rare species who will always be learning to his last breath, a man of inborn wonder. So he tells a workman to stretch the guts along the dock and wind them back and forth between two upright poles and measure the total length. The man shrugs—*Porque no?*—and unwinds the long pink tube. He frees it from the filmy membrane with his sharp knife and starts to walk away with the upper end. His amazement grows as he pulls at the endless coil. When the last bit is free—that end which is the size of a stovepipe—the total length is twelve hundred feet. He reports to the manager, who can't believe it, and figures it out for himself. It's true! In later years the manager reads a book on whales, but he never learns why the sperm whale has a quarter-mile of guts, for no book has the answer.

The American commercial attaché in the nearest city hears about the whale and visits the reduction plant with an odd request. If more whales are captured, would it be possible to freeze the meat for sale to his government? In the state of Florida the department of agriculture is raising screwworms on whale meat. Screwworms, the larvae of a kind of fly, are a serious pest in the southeast, for they burrow into the flesh of cattle, and they can kill a full-grown steer in less than ten days. When the flies are newly hatched, they are sterilized with gamma radiation and the impotent insects dumped from airplanes over the infested states. The sterile flies mate with wild ones, and eggs are laid, but they never hatch. Slowly the wild population is being thinned out, and soon the native flies will find no mates at all. The scourge will be gone. In the meanwhile, the program calls for many millions of dollars and many tons of whale meat.

The manager of the plant is amused. He calls the foreman. The two men break into a rapid discussion. Finally the manager turns to the attaché. We are sorry, he says, but the supply of whales here is not reliable. And the climate is so warm that the meat may spoil and the little flies will not like to eat it. And though the freezer plant is working fine today it may be broken down tomorrow. The attaché understands; he thanks them and goes away.

MARCH

WITHIN the herd of several hundred whales that includes the Little Calf and his mother a restless spirit is beginning to brush the body of this one and that. Indeed the tempo and behavior of the whole herd is beginning to change. This is more than a response to the gusty, brawling winds of March. It is a deep, biological pricking that swells the testes of the males and rouses the ovaries of the females and causes both males and females to move in patterns unaccustomed for a year. In May the testes of the bulls will ripen to a weight of sixty pounds or more—seven gallons in size. Already these organs are beginning to fatten, and the sperm cells within are multiplying and maturing. In the ovaries of the females the follicles are quickening and here and there a germ center is building the shape and structure of an egg.

As in all animals on earth, the body of the whale contains a biological clock, and when the alarm sounds the body tissues respond in predictable ways and the body motions follow suit. The unseen force now sounding the alarm for the family of the Little Calf is the growing length of day. As the broad white daylight impinges on the eye of the whale it excites a gland no bigger than a crab apple in the brain, the gland secretes a chemical messenger to the blood, and the messenger flows to the sex organs and to all the other tissues of the body. The grand, complex, ritual procession of the breeding season begins to move. The insurance of the species begins to pay.

Little Calf

(Among the Stone Age Eskimo that Vilhjalmur Stefansson and Peter Freuchen knew, the return of the spring sun after four months of night was the signal for a resurgence of sex. Any parallel with whales is superficial, though; "exuberance" —known to men—does not apply to whales.)

The herd now sorts itself into groups or camps. The adolescent males of ten years or so, and the older males, too, pull away from the herd, swimming faster, moving northward at a greater pace. The younger males are in the lead; the older ones are delayed by battling. The Little Calf grows used to the underwater sounds of challenge and the thump of bodies and the gurgle of air expelled from the lungs of struggling males. Most of the battles are contests of pure bluff, sham affairs in which no blood is shed and no bones are broken.

The females, too, sense the changes in March: the increase in volume and pitch of the submarine talk and the swirl of dark bodies. Some of them feel a rising tension in their own frames. They move northward toward the waters off southern California. In some mysterious way each female knows her own time.

The Little Calf has often sported with another calf of his own age, a little female. Lately he is puzzled by her strange behavior. What is wrong? She engages in play but after a moment she turns to the mother of the Little Calf and pushes angrily at her breast. She gets a few swallows of milk and then the mother pulls away and slaps the alien baby with her flipper.

The thin, sad baby lost her own mother in an accident at sea three weeks ago and is now dying of dehydration, though she is immersed in the sea. Some basic sense of rightness re-

100

moved from what we humans call compassion warns the Little Calf's mother that the species is more important than the individual. She knows her own calf; she nurses it for the allotted time; she will not nurse a calf with foreign voice and feel. This is the law. The orphan is doomed.

Today the shifting winds and the sea currents and the flowing streams of life-providing food of the sea have worked together to bring the family of the Little Calf to a point two miles west of Isla de Guadalupe, which is a barren scabland one hundred and fifty miles at sea off Baja California, which is a bleak but hauntingly beautiful part of Mexico.

I find myself again, as in a dream, on that tiny island where I landed once to look at the last of the Guadalupe fur seals. Here on a hot, dry slope, a landscape from hell, I stare at circles and squares of piled-up rocks, the walls of huts erected in the 1800s by whalers. The roofs I suppose would have been sailcloth, stretched tightly above the walls, with a space to vent the suffocating air. Scratched on the gray volcanic rocks I read the names of ships and men, clear names in the beautiful curving script of their time. The oldest I find is "*Ship Essex . . . Henry Waldbon . . . Bristol R I . . . 1835.*"

I stand in the shimmering heat, removed in time a century and more. The ghostly figures of bearded men in rough, sour clothes pass before my eyes. They speak directly of their captain: "Where does the sonofabitch think we're gonna sleep?" The pattern of seafaring men does not change.

Aside from its history—and of course its seals—the island is a lost place. Created in eons past by volcanic fire, with jagged red-and-black beds of rocks and leering gargoyles of lava, it rises four thousand feet above the sea. The north, and highest, point is often hidden in a cloud, and from this misty source a trickle of water finds its way to the ocean in certain months of the year.

The land animals are wild goats, cats, and mice—nothing more. All were dumped here by man and all have reverted to a wild and desperate state, and all are struggling to live on this rugged, almost treeless rock. Driven by hunger, a goat inched its way along a crumbling ledge toward the last spear of green, suddenly to fall to its death. I see its bones, and bones by the hundreds, where the sea currents have washed them ashore in quiet coves. I photograph the pattern of white skeletons curled there, for I like the design. I put aside for a moment the thought of man's stupidity in bringing the beasts to the island in the first place.

The pathetic mummy of a house mouse is impaled on a cactus spine where the little beast tried to reach a succulent bit of green within. (I remember some words by Peter Crowcroft, director of the Brookfield Zoo in Chicago, in *Mice All Over:* "There is something terribly familiar about the awful situation of a mouse in the world.") Bleached, white, feather-filled droppings of cats are scattered around the mouths of tunnels where petrels are still trying to nest.

Were it not for the seals and the trickle of fresh water, I am sure that hot, dry, stinking Guadalupe would never have lured the *Essex* to drop anchor off its shores.

Toward evening, off Guadalupe, the Little Calf is surrounded by a chorus of dolphin music of extraordinary richness and volume. It swells from, and through, and above a chance aggregation of seven species of dolphins, some of them in schools of hundreds. The larger schools are breeding groups; the smaller schools are only passing through. Within a radius of a mile two thousand black-and-white bodies criss-cross the upper layer of the sea, where a vast cloud of pink plankton has risen as dusk falls, and where fish in turn have gathered to feed upon the plankton life. It is a mild evening, for March. The ocean is alive with splashing forms.

In the frenzy of sexual and social excitement some of the dolphins find partners of other (though closely related) species, and next year there will be born little hybrids that will puzzle a Japanese biologist when he finds the carcasses of odd pattern in his net.

The Little Calf can scarcely hear the sound of his own family in the din of the dolphins underwater as they locate food and talk to each other, coming and going at high speed. The Little Calf knows all the sounds, though he has never heard so many at once. The crack of a shot, followed by the rattle of an explosion, shakes his inner ear and reverberates from the ceiling of plankton.

Motorcyclists roar in along the beach from the east and disappear toward the west. Through a powerful background murmur there burst sad howlings, shriekings, and lowing sounds like cattle in distress.

The sperm whales continue on their course and by midnight have left the center of sound behind. They are in quieter surroundings. En route they pick up a few of the pilchards, anchovies, and lantern fish upon which the dolphins are also feeding, though these small fishes hold only passing interest for the great whales.

Toward dawn on the last day of March the wet sea fog begins to lift. The world becomes three parts: black beneath, gray above, and white between. Dainty sandpipers rise and fall on the ocean swell and peep softly as the tone of illumination changes.

One of the sperm whales sees a ruddy glow on the horizon, though indeed not in the east where the sun should be rising. With food in mind, he swims toward it for a mile until he catches a vagrant breeze and finds himself at the edge of a foul streamer of smoke pouring from the center of the glow. He snorts in fright and turns away.

The refrigerator ship *Shoku Maru* is wallowing in a fourteen-foot swell. She is alone and all aflame; a fire in her hold is out of control. Her crew left yesterday in life rafts, with a Buddhist prayer. Now they drift toward the west, waiting for the American Coast Guard to pick them up. They open wood-veneer boxes of salt fish and dried seaweed and rice. They hope to be saved, for before the captain ordered "abandon ship" the radioman told the world in broken English of their plight. The message spread over the globe in a tenth of a second. It was heard in silence by a yeoman at Byrd Station, near Little America, and by seafaring men on a dozen seas. It was heard by ship brokers in Tokyo, and the stock of Matsushita broke half a point.

Kasuo Fujima opens a roll of cloth in his kit and removes a length of cod line with triple hooks. He baits the hooks with salt fish and drops them over the edge of the raft. The baits rise and fall two hundred feet below. They move there for an hour and wash clean and white. Fujima-san pulls in the line. No one says a word. When a great ship is passing from the world it is like the passing of a sweetheart. One pauses, and tries desperately to store an image of beauty in a recess of the mind where it can be recovered.

Now and then a gray, sloppy sea slaps at the hull of the rolling *Shoku* and leaps beyond, to the fiery core of her distress, and the water bursts into a tower of red. A muffled explosion throws a rocket of white lines high into the fading night. In another hour a metal seam will buckle with a popping of rivets and the ship will die in a hell of sound and light, and her black form will slide mercifully down to the floor of the sea.

APRIL

THE family of the Little Calf is now feeding near latitude Thirty North, northwest of Isla de Guadalupe and south of the Channel Islands of California. Young and old have come nine hundred miles on a meandering course since they left the scene of the battle of the bulls in early January. They have joined a herd so large that from a ship the white streams of vapor seem to cover the whole western ocean and continue beyond the horizon.

In the north the sky is darkening. Late in the afternoon a bull marked by a white spot about the size of a dinner plate on the middle of his back—a mass of scar tissue from an old wound—swims for a minute beside another bull, then turns away and follows a cow. Hour after hour the pair swim side by side, keeping touch by flippers and flukes, or simply rubbing sides. They are silent. Neither feeds; neither dives, though they run submerged for minutes at a time. Presently the male moves to a position above the female, gently stroking her back. He withdraws and chases her for five minutes. (There is no question about who is the aggressor.) He speeds up and rubs his belly against hers in a burst of motion. Now he races ahead and rolls, exposing first his belly and then his back. He shoots through the water with his flippers held stiffly at right angles to his sides. He is simply throwing his body into odd shapes to attract the female. The tempo of courtship rises. The cow turns responsively upside down and the bull swims across her inflamed belly. They return to normal swimming positions and the bull locks his jaw in hers. They nuzzle, clap jaws, slam their heads together. The love play continues for half an hour.

The black cloud from the north is drawing close and the edge of the sea is hidden in a veil of rain.

At last the pair rise high from the sea, black snouts against black sky, belly to belly, flippers touching, water draining from the warm, clean flanks. They copulate in seconds, then fall heavily into the sea with a resounding splash.

The herd is moving north or northwest at an average speed of three knots, about as fast as a man could walk. In a few days a pattern begins to take shape in the movements of each individual whale. The blowhole flares and closes; the eye seems to wink; the sudden flash of long furrows in the skin suggests the play of muscles underneath. The Little Calf is nursing; his mother warily keeps her distance from the rest of the group.

In the midst of the wind and the rain another pair of whales also mates, this time in the horizontal position.

Then the sea is blotted out by the storm.

MAY

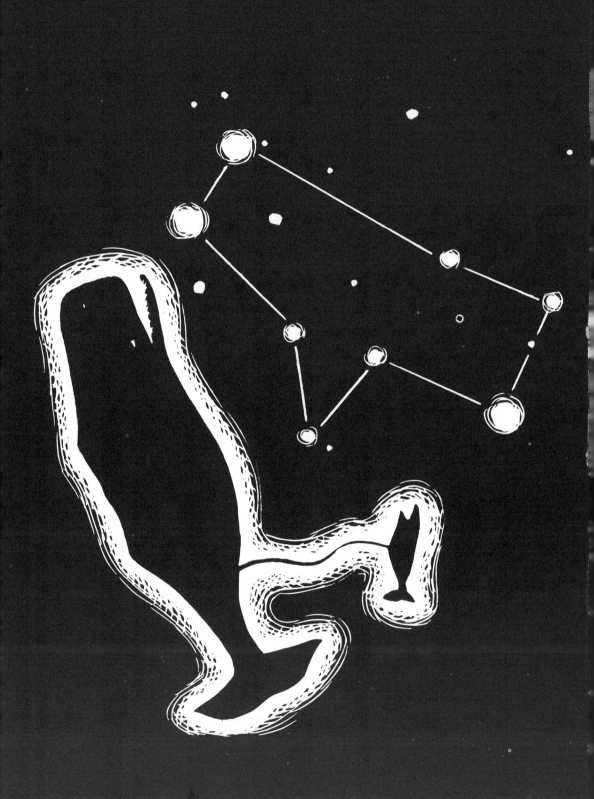

THE Little Calf is now eight months old. A human child at this age is trying to lift its body from the floor, to cling briefly to chairs, and to reach for the hem of mother's skirt. The Little Calf, by contrast, is well along the road to independence; if his mother were to disappear overnight he might perhaps survive alone.

The Little Calf and his mother are feeding four hundred miles at sea off San Francisco. They will go no farther north this year, though many of their companions have dropped from sight over the horizon, far on their way to the Bering Sea. The females that came into heat have dallied behind. The pattern of the herd as the Little Calf knew it in spring is dissolving. Whales of like age and sex and breeding disposition are now consorting; the groups are separating in space because of the differences in their swimming speeds.

The day is mild. A filmy diffusion pales the blue of the sky and gives a soft extra light. A gentle breeze touches the moving sea. Here and there the surface breaks in a pattern of light, struck by a shower of needles. Schools of sauries, each holding a million fish, break and boil to the top. Their sides are gleaming iridescent silver; their backs are metallic blue-green. The Little Calf and his mother, along with seven other females, the harem bull, and a young male, are lazily following the fish, feasting as they go. During the bright of day, when the schools descend for reasons of their own—reasons unknown to man—the old whales pursue them down, while during the night the young whales plunge with open jaws through the silver masses. Even the Little Calf, though nursing, is swallowing the fat, tasty, ten-inch fish.

At 9:43 in the morning the silver aircraft *Clipper Dawn*, en route from San Francisco to Honolulu, appears low down in the eastern sky and begins to chalk a clean white line across the blue-black vault.

And at 9:43 a whale in the family of the Little Calf is in distress.

For several weeks the Little Calf has been aware of two grown females in the family who are traveling together at the edge of the group. Their bellies are rounded, especially the belly of one. She is, in fact, the youngish female who carries the two-foot length of swordfish bill embedded in her hump. She is about to give birth to her first calf, and all is not going well. On either side of her lower belly the outline of a breast shows clearly as an oval pad, five feet long. Her navel bulges like a white fist. She is tense, irritable, clumsy. She bends her long trunk and tail at right angles to her body and whips them back again. The slit of her vagina flares pink from time to time. The taut outer profile of her flank changes visibly, rippling and bulging as the fetus changes position in her womb.

When she slows her swimming speed and begins to twist near the surface of the sea, four other whales move in, drawn by an excitement as old as life itself. A young male, puzzled, or perhaps annoyed, by the strange behavior of the female, butts her rudely under the left flipper and she brings the limb down with a stunning blow across his eye. The whales circle the female, talking in ultrasound and giving also the rare, shrill buzz, audible to man, which springs from the blowhole with a stream of bubbles. The young mother-to-be is breathing heavily.

At 9:53 the gray folded tail flukes of a calf appear at the birth opening, then retreat. They slowly reappear. The mother contorts her body to the limit of its bulky shape and jerks her tail convulsively. The gray-and-black infant slides out rapidly until the flippers are due to come. (At this level of the baby's body the girth is greatest, or about what a man could circle with his arms.) Here the flippers catch in the opening; the body hangs. The little thing is now clearly a male.

Minutes pass. The mother twists and the calf twists, though his movements grow slower and more feeble. The pair rise and fall in the gentle sea. At 10:46 the mother, still submerged, makes a deep contraction and expels her breath. Instantly the calf is hidden in a cloud of pink. Now he is clear, swimming actively. The mother whirls. The cord stretches and snaps near her belly. In less than a minute the calf is at the surface gasping for air. The muscles of the mother's belly stiffen and contract; the placenta is expelled. She ignores it. (Were she a land mammal she might have eaten it. Land creatures do this, it is said, to destroy an odorous thing which could attract predators to the nest or den and also to restore to the mother some of the nutrients spent in pregnancy.) For an hour blood dribbles from the new mother.

Up above, on the breezy surface of the ocean, the black backs of the whales continue to circle. A score of shearwaters are drawn to the scene, the first of millions now winging their way northward from the nesting season in Bass Strait and

Little Calf

among the Islands of Magellan. They skim on rakish black wings only inches above the water, back and forth above the whales. Finding no food, they wheel about and press toward their rendezvous in the sea pastures of Alaska. Soon the Little Calf will see ten thousand birds a day coursing above his feeding grounds.

One hour and three minutes the mother whale was in labor. Though her calf was born early in the season and was slow in coming, he seems to be normal and healthy. He swims now beneath her tail and searches blindly for the nipples. The mother touches him often and tenderly with her sensitive flipper but makes no effort to help him find the place. His right flipper is still crimped from confinement in the womb; he swims lamely. When he strays off into the blue dimness his mother is quickly at his side, nudging him gently. She is a new creature, active, responsive, a ton lighter in weight. Not until evening, when the shadow of the great form beside him is growing vague, does her calf find the soft place on her belly which will be the focus of his waking hours for two years to come.

JUNE

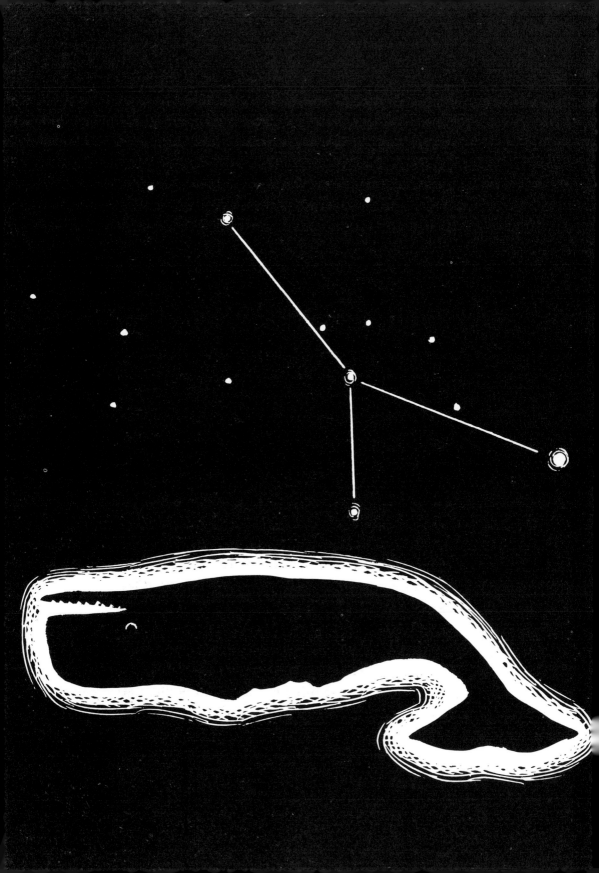

ᴇARLY in June the Little Calf, still with his mother on the western side of the broad Pacific Ocean, is swimming slowly, approaching with caution a large floating mass that echoes "whale" but yet not the kind of whale he knows. He moves toward the quiet thing. It rises and falls, inert. He turns his snout to right and left, bringing into play all senses. (Mother has moved along a hundred yards.) There it lies—gray, speckled with white. One long flipper dips into the sea and the other stands rakishly in the air like a last call for help. The open belly is a thicket of trailing tissues and, through the tissues, three sleeper sharks wind back and forth with cold eyes, tearing now and then as appetite urges. The thing is a dead humpback whale. It is sixty feet long, toothless like all of its kind, and also eyeless, because swimming crabs have chewed the lenses from their sockets. The great carcass is barely awash. Soon a shark will puncture the arching back and then the thing will settle imperceptibly to the bottom. There a hundred blind scavengers of a hundred sizes will penetrate its flesh and leave at last a skeleton. The hard, white, stony ear bones, the size of a man's fist, will persist for a few decades. Perhaps at last a scientific boat, a deep-sea dredger, will haul these curious bones to the top, though probably the chance is very remote.

A pair of dolphins—harlequins in black and white, perfect in form and splendid in motion—approach the Little

Little Calf

Calf. They leap full fifteen feet into the blue, throwing a haze of crystal sparks. To the Little Calf, they are part of the world. They wave and twist ahead in rushing flight, joyous.

Softly the Little Calf sinks. He has no limits. He is in balance with time and space. Infinite time and planetary space are nothing. He stares sleepily into the soft blue growing darker blue and purple black. The pressure gains. He stops. He moves a lazy tail and gently rises to the top. He breathes a dozen drafts.

An hour later, he is loafing near the bright top of the sea. He has filled his belly again with warm, yellow milk and now he tugs gently at the tail of a large fish, a mahimahi, that protrudes from mother's mouth. Is she deliberately teaching him to take solid food? This is doubtful. At any rate, he tears off a delicious chunk of white meat and gulps it down.

An hour after sunset the mother of the Little Calf arches her back and begins her first descent of the day to the deeper feeding layers. Tonight is her lucky night, for in less than a minute she finds herself at the edge of a cloud of luminescent squids. What they lack in size they make up in number; thousands upon thousands of blue-white shapes darting swiftly through the dark. Turning and twisting blindly she seizes a dozen elusive forms in her mouth and crushes them to a mass. She relaxes. Some of the glowing phosphorescent slime from their skin spreads over the lining of her mouth and clings to her teeth and tongue. She slides quietly through the sea. Squids, and the predatory fishes which pursue them, are attracted to the pale cavern of her mouth and, as they come within range, she bites them easily. When she rises at last to blow and belch, the Little Calf is there at the surface to greet

120

her. He is excited by the ghostly fire that gleams from the angle of her jaws, for he has seen it before and he associates it with food. On her next dive he follows her uncertainly down.

In the meanwhile, the squids have moved up to within a hundred feet of the surface, where they are now feeding on plankton. Hugging his mother's flank, the Little Calf sees a submarine world at night as a dim shadowy mist pierced by jerking blobs of light. He seizes a pale fragment that curls from his mother's mouth and finds it good. His excitement grows. He cleaves the water in a surge of power and his toothless jaws clamp firmly on two of the squids. Now his lungs are feeling the strain and he moves upward. Up and down he travels for a long while, feeding and breathing, making four round trips to his mother's one.

Quite suddenly he is full. He floats at the surface under the stars, drifting now into sleep and then briefly out to move a flipper idly and bring his nostril into the cool sea breeze. Toward daybreak his mother approaches and tests him with the quiet humming of her inner voice. She retreats. For the first time in his short life the Little Calf will not awaken for his morning milk.

Last November in the year of the whale the Little Calf's half-sister who was caught for Life Arena had survived the hardships of capture and greedily started swallowing an artificial diet resembling her mother's milk. She was the first sperm whale ever to live in captivity.

Now, half a year later, she is swimming in a measured circle in her green pool; waiting for her morning meal. The staff of the aquarium have named her "Susie" after a slender black-haired girl who has come to Life Arena once or twice a week throughout her high-school career. "Crazy about animals," they say of the girl Susie. She works without pay, feeding the porpoises, scrubbing the glass walls of the fish tanks, and nursing the so-called orphan seals that well-meaning people bring to Life Arena in summer in the delusion that they have been abandoned. Often she simply sits dreamily watching the animals or sketching the attitudes they take.

The moment that Susie saw the young sperm whale sliding through the water, a rapport began to grow between them, a bond stronger than the feeling of the whale for the men in uniform upon whom she depended for food.

Now in June the captive whale has just been weaned from her liquid diet at twenty months or so. (The men at Life Arena try to guess her age.) She may have been weaned too early. She weighs only two tons and is in fact underweight, though on a rich diet of a hundred pounds a day she is fast nearing the normal size of a sperm-whale youngster in the open sea.

Most of her food is opalescent squid, a kind of soft, naked, free-swimming mollusk that swarms in Monterey Bay. Its body, eight inches long, is milky-translucent, faintly bluish, with brilliant blue-green spots that blaze and fade and run in rippling waves along the pale skin. In early summer the squids gather to mate and then to lay their eggs on the sandy rims of the submarine canyons of the Bay. Then the fishermen come at night with lampara nets and purse seines and flashing lights to harvest them by the thousands of tons. Some of the catch is frozen in blocks of ice and trucked to nearby Life Arena, where it is fed to Susie the Whale.

At first she stubbornly refused to eat the squids. Week after week the patient keepers tried to slip the solid food into her gullet at nursing time. She quickly learned their game and jerked away. In desperation they sent a refrigerated tank-truck to the Bay and returned with a thousand living squids which they poured into her pool. At first she was frightened by the flashing forms. Then she began to play with them, snapping her jaws like a dog at a window pane trying to catch blue-bottle flies. At the end of the week, the keepers cut her milk supply in half. Susie the Whale was disturbed. She swam constantly. Then she began to swallow some of the squids whose fleshy forms she had up to now been content simply to crush.

When Susie first learned to feed, she was briefly a television star. A cameraman, sweating with exertion and fright in a rubber suit, followed her around the tank, catching the images of white squids drifting like snow across the dark opening of her mouth. In two dramatic weeks she was weaned from milk to living squids, and then to freshly thawed squids dumped from the keeper's bucket.

Susie the Girl could not keep away from her namesake. But a note from school suggested that perhaps she was neglecting her homework. Reluctantly she turned to the gray world imposed by adults for the two remaining weeks of school.

In the meantime, she had moved far in her groping effort to *reach* the little whale, to strengthen the bond of communication. She had learned to scrub the sensitive snout with a brush. Garbed in a sweatshirt and faded jeans, she had learned to hold a rubber tire and to let the whale struggle with toothless jaws to tear it from her grasp. (The contest was always short and in favor of the whale.) After long deliberation, the

123

manager of Life Arena gave in to her latest bold request: to ride on the back of Susie the Whale.

It proved to be no trick at all. In the open sea, the wild young sperm whales often wrestle with each other (if I may use this word to describe the sliding, rolling, pounding games of body contact they play). So the transfer from whale-against-whale to girl-on-tail really broke no rule in the instinctive code of Susie the Whale. The keeper stood by tensely, boat hook in hand, as the girl slipped into the water. More in excitement than in fear, she pushed her palms against the black flukes. The whale turned half circle in mild surprise, then paused to blow. Spitting water, the girl scrambled to the top of the tapering trunk, gripping the slippery skin with her knees, and rose triumphantly. There she swayed for a long moment, black hair streaming, arms outstretched, a figure from a Cretan vase—twenty-five centuries full circle!

JULY

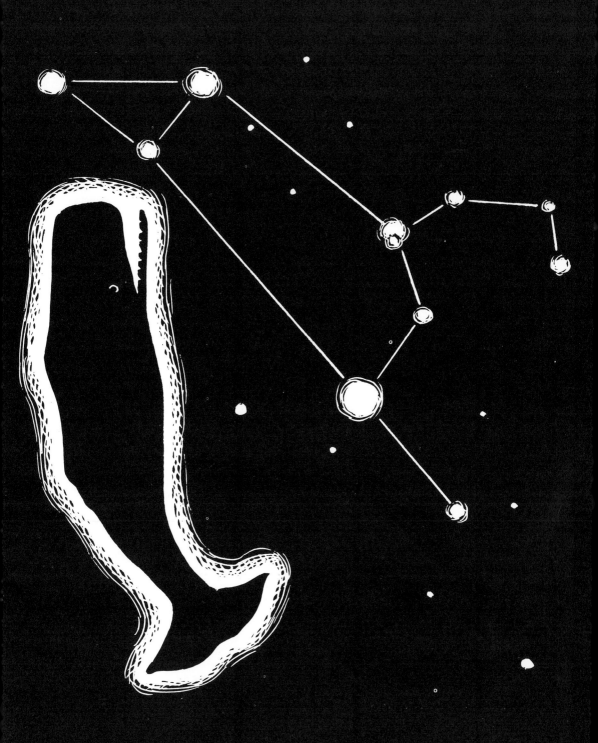

IN the year of the whale there are days when nothing is new. On such a day in July the air is filled with a monotonous hissing of sound as one rain squall pursues another across the dappled sea. The Little Calf swims beneath his mother's body in a dark shadow illuminated at the edges by a blue-gray light from above. Subconsciously he tries to match the rhythmic, undulating sameness of her body, for the beating impulses of her flesh and the surrounding water have been one great throbbing part of his life from its beginning. In trying to keep pace, he sometimes falls behind and must sprint for a dozen strokes to re-enter the comforting zone of shadow. When she pauses to rest near the surface he rubs the corner of his mouth against her nipples to stimulate the flow of milk. Half-asleep, she nurses him for a few minutes, then rouses and moves along. Toward evening, she leaves him in the care of other adults and begins to dive for food.

The year of the whale resembles the year of man a thousand centuries ago, when life was plain and brutish and progress was measured in simple terms of staying alive. Now humans crowd more and more into a single life, ask for excitement to the point of stress, and often go beyond. If, by some magic of electronics, man could spy on the intimate life of a whale, even for a week, he would turn away, bored and restless.

127

Little Calf

On the next day, the sun shines again and the Little Calf is in playful mood. The family overtakes a drifting set of heavy planks all bound together like a raft—a hatch cover torn by storm from the deck of a steamer in a distant sea. The thing is ten feet square and it rides heavily on the swell. Gooseneck barnacles hang beneath it in the green shade and tirelessly comb the water with their fringes. Tube worms and a dozen kinds of green and brown and red seaweeds trail and twist in the stream, while creatures no larger than matchheads browse like tiny goats among the foliage.

The Little Calf slides beneath the sluggish raft, rubbing the skin of his back along the brushy texture. He boosts it and enjoys the splash as it falls back. He turns and hits it harder and wallows and tumbles in pleasure and finally flops the thing completely over. Two other young whales join in the sport. They play until exhausted, not as much from muscle tiredness as from overheating. They have no sweat glands. The outer skin and the flippers and the tail surfaces begin to flush and the temperatures rise within the warm coats of insulating blubber until at last the little whales have had enough. All but the Little Calf. He is now eleven months old. In a final rush of spirit he takes off at top speed toward the distant sound of mother's voice and all at once he is a flying whale, airborne for the first time, skimming a full three seconds above the sea in a sparkling shower of light.

He rests beside his mother. Flitting shadows touch his head and he rolls easily to one side to look upward. The source of the shadows is gone already down the line of vision. Clean white birds beat the air with rhythmic, tireless wings. Seven arctic terns, streamer-tailed relatives of the gulls, speed to their nesting grounds at the tundra edge of melting snow. Ten thousand miles they wing their way from Antarctic to Arctic in the northern summer and ten thousand miles return in fall. All this on a few ounces of fuel—an incredible voyage.

Their frail bodies are buffeted by wind, but they move on a steady course toward the north. They pause to rest every thousand miles or so, dropping lightly to flotsam on the water, to a log or a raft of kelp. (They hesitate to wet their breasts on the sea itself.) Soon they will reach a gravel beach along a wild clean Alaskan stream and there they will lay their eggs on the bare rocks.

The Little Calf also knows the other terns—the sooty terns. Now in July these handsome black-and-white relations of the arctic tribe are nesting a million strong on oceanic islands of the Pacific. I write of the sooty terns with great wonder, for they stay aloft for months on end, with no cushion but the air, or such, at least, is the evidence. Men do not see the terns at rest outside the breeding season, and, what is more, the feet and feathers of the birds do not seem well adapted for life on the sea. I tire to think of their tireless circles far above the world.

The eastern limit of the sea pasture in which the Little Calf and his family are feeding today is the coastal strip of central California. This humid strip is the habitat or native haunt of a peculiar race of men who see in any new event, in any change of circumstance, a potential source of dollar revenue. They speak of the "fast buck," though only to members of their own kind. To others they speak of "opportunity," "advancement," "progress," or "improvement." Each member of the race has an angle. His delight is to guess the other's angle while concealing his own.

All this sets the stage for a certain July event.

During the night, a dead sperm whale floats on a flood tide to a beach north of the Golden Gate. It is a small whale, only twenty-two feet long. It comes to rest in a fog. No one knows it is there until a beachcomber, searching for glass balls and odd bits of driftwood, sees the dark thing in the surf at four in the morning. He rubs his eyes, then runs to a seaside cafe that serves early breakfast to the perch fishermen. He calls his friend McGill. McGill is a member of the special race. He runs a tourist trap at Sausalito. It sits beside the road, and its on-and-off red light should be a warning to navigators of the road but instead it lures them in. Here they buy souvenirs of the West (made in Japan and Czechoslovakia). They buy delicate carvings on genuine simulated ivory depicting an Eskimo pressing his sledge dogs to the limit (made ten at a time with a master template and a routing machine in a Market Street basement).

McGill rouses from sleep and gets the message. At once alert, his eyes glisten and shift; a fleeting smile crosses his lips. "Be right over," he says as he jumps into his pants. "Get back and stake out a claim on that there whale!"

The beachcomber is paid off with a five-dollar bill and a share of stock in McGill Enterprises (worth perhaps a dollar and a half), and soon McGill himself has the whale on a truck, towing it to Santa Clarissima. Here he bargains with a mortician to embalm it. The mortician, too, is one of the fast-buck race. He telephones to a supplier; he orders more formalin-and-mercury than a respectable undertaker would use in a disaster.

After an all-night operation the whale is rigid. A blue-

130

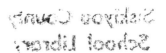

gray film settles over its eyes and its tongue pulls back in a queer triangle, though no one knows the difference. McGill hoses the body down and covers it with a tarpaulin, then heads for the nearest sign shop.

In just thirty-six hours after it stranded in the haunts of California man, the whale stares into the distance, resting on the truck, while above it a sign proclaims:

BIGGEST LIVING THING ON EARTH   TOUCH IT   FEEL IT
A FULL-GROWN WHALE FROM THE ABISMAL DEPTHS
OF THE SEA   THE LEVIATHAN OF HOLY WRIT
ONE DAY ONLY   ONE DOLLAR

Each night the truck moves in darkness to a roadside stand at the edge of a small town and each morning the flow of visitors begins. The whale is a gold mine. July turns to August, and the thermometer climbs to one hundred and five. An ineffable vapor rises from the patient corpse. When McGill eats a hamburger it tastes like whale and when he eats an egg it tastes like whale. During the day he begins to hate this whale and in his dreams at night he is pursued by whales in great variety, all of which he hates.

The exhibit is shopworn, too. Along its graying sides are carved initials, and the names of motorcycle gangs and schools and lovers and political candidates. The eyes have long since disappeared and a half-dozen teeth have been pried loose behind McGill's back.

When the whiskey, too, begins to taste like whale, McGill is alarmed. He changes the sign to

FOR SALE, YOUR PRICE

but he has no offer. The town marshal suggests that perhaps

131

the whale has outstayed its welcome, though the marshal personally has nothing against a good, clean, educational-type exhibit. McGill has in mind a solution. It is typical of his kind to anticipate a way out, with several good alternatives.

That night he drives a hundred miles to a lookout point on the Palisade Drive. He loosens the fastenings on the whale, backs the truck swiftly to the concrete guardrail and jumps on the brake as the rear tires hit. The truck rears like a frightened mustang and its burden slides into empty space. Ages later (it seems) a distant crash merges with the sound of the booming surf and the whale returns to its primordial home.

AUGUST

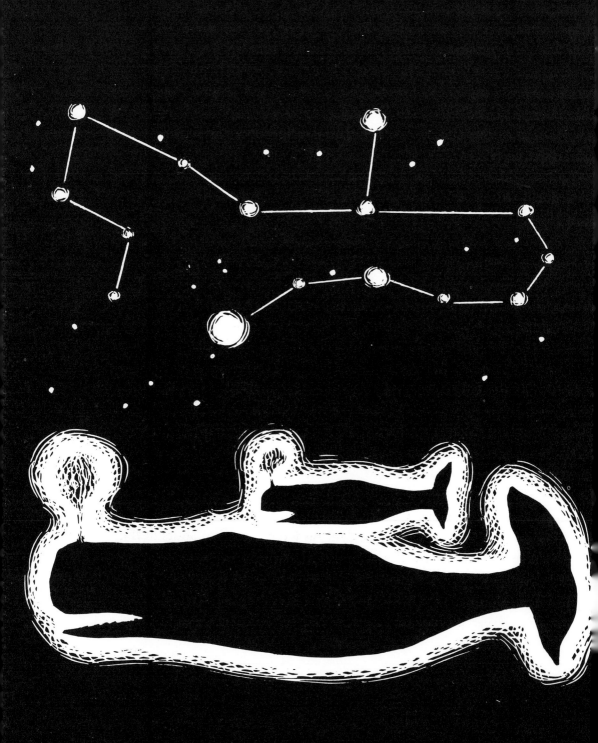

THE year of the whale draws to a close. The Little Calf has grown six feet in body length and has gained twelve hundred pounds. He will nurse for another year, though several months before his mother's breasts turn dry he will be feeding largely for himself. His weaning will come about through a mutual loss of interest between mother and calf; she irritated by the butting of the three- or four-ton baby and he annoyed by the trickle of milk that fails to satisfy his surging appetite. The fall season will find mother and calf in waters north of the Hawaiian Islands. The mother will not come in heat this year; she will have no urge to join the noisy harem on the Tropic of Cancer where last September she gave birth to the Little Calf.

In August the sperm whales of the North Pacific are widely scattered from the equator to the Bering Sea. Half of them are south of the Great Circle between southern California and southern Japan, and half are north. This imaginary "half-the-population line" will soon drop south and in March will turn north again.

In the Arctic Ocean, long crooked channels of blue water spread daily between the drifting ice cakes. The limits of the ice retreat toward the Pole. For another month, into September, the edge of the pack will crumble under the rays of the sun. Now if ever is the season when the stout ships of the polar scientists pass from the North Atlantic to the North Pacific, and vice versa, above the continents of the Old World and the New. In September the earth will turn the corner of its path around the sun and the days will shorten. A film of new sea ice will form each night between the floes, and gradually the great white polar sheet will creep south again through the Chukchi Sea and into the Bering.

In August now a solitary sperm whale has reached the northern limit of his range; he is feeding off Cape Navarin at Sixty-two North. The sudden flowering of his breath stands white in the cold air. He sees a solitary iceberg drifting quietly in the last stages of decay, far from the pack, riddled and channeled by sun and rain. At one edge it is stained brown where a walrus family rested a month ago and many miles away. The bull whale rises from a feeding dive with a trail of gray mud clouding the water behind him, for the Bering Sea is shallow here. (The sea floor was dry land thirty thousand years ago, when the first Americans walked across it from Asia.) The bull crowds to the limit of his chilly range, not because it is comfortable but because the food is rich. He finds a wealth of squid and also creatures of the bottom that he rarely feasts on in the North Pacific: crabs, octopus, and dogfish sharks.

At Life Arena, Susie the Girl is working for the summer as a Visitor Guide—her first paid job. Two physiologists from a nearby university have arrived with a mass of equipment: glassware and tubing, metal frames, adhesives, devices with numbered dials, batteries, and a hundred odds and ends. They are planning some experiments on Susie the Whale to get data on how whales keep warm in cold water and how they cool off after they have exercised.

Peter Skansen and John Cantwell have studied heat regulation in animals for many years. They have sweated together in the Mojave Desert, looking at lizards and snakes, and they have shivered together at Cape Crozier, looking at penguins and seals. Most of what they know of heat regulation in whales has been learned by crude methods: pushing thermometers into freshly killed animals at whaling stations; dissecting carcasses. Once a female finback was stranded near John's summer cottage and stayed alive on the beach a day and a half. They put thermometers into her body openings, and after she died took chunks of fresh tissue to preserve for study. They also experimented by putting blocks of ice into a tank with a porpoise and found that the animal shivered for a while, then, in effect, its body thermostat clicked on. In a few minutes it seemed normal.

Now, having heard that Susie the Whale is partly tamed, they propose to find out what she can tell them—indirectly— about her body heat exchange. They explain their purpose to the manager and the veterinarian of Life Arena, with Susie the Girl listening.

The manager is eager to help. "You know, gentlemen, zoo-keeping is a strange mixture of show business and science. We always have to think of money, expenses, the budget. But we have a real appetite for new ideas about animals. There is no money in zoo-keeping; our satisfaction comes from trying to bring man into sympathy with the animals that outnumber him a million to one. Tell us what we can do for you."

"Well, first, how much do you estimate that Susie weighs?"

"Maybe two tons, and she's eating a hundred pounds a day."

Skansen scribbles on the back of an envelope. "Then I

figure she needs about fifteen thousand calories a day, or roughly six times the demand of a man. But this suggests that she's eating too much. Hm-m-m . . . wet food . . . some of it probably lost in the pool . . ."

The questions continue. The scientists learn that Susie the Whale is most relaxed and least excited by visitors to Life Arena, on Monday mornings. They learn how far Susie the Girl has gone in her effort to reach the whale; to what extent she has been able to manipulate her; what she has accomplished in her attempts to touch sensitive parts like the blowhole and the belly.

Now Pete, grinning, pulls out an FM transmitter from his bag of scientific gear and places it against his own stomach. *Beep-beep-beep* . . . It sounds a clear signal. "I tried this gadget on myself," he says. "I swallowed it after breakfast this morning. It's a remote-sensing thermistor in a capsule about the size of my thumb. I would say that, by now, it's right about here"—pointing.

So on Monday at dawn, Pete and John, Susie the Girl, and a keeper are feeding the little whale. They hide a thermistor in the belly of a herring. Susie the Whale gulps it down without a pause. But she is not so sure that all is well when Susie the Girl slips long metal thermometers into her vaginal opening and her rectum; she is definitely nervous when Susie places a soft rubber cup, like a "plumber's friend," over her blowhole. This breathing pore is the portal of life itself. By a sensitive, palpating, pleading approach to the whale's mouth, Susie succeeds in holding a thermometer under her tongue for thirty seconds, which is long enough for the scientists. Now through the rubber cup on the nostril a sample of gases in and out is being collected.

138

"Watch out for the loose stuff!" cautions the manager. "We don't want her to swallow any hardware." He knows from long experience that animals in zoos and aquariums will pick up bottles and bottle tops, coins, combs, plastic toys, all the debris that thoughtless visitors toss within their reach.

Susie the Whale is growing restless. She slaps her tail smartly on the surface. She gently seizes the arm of her friend Susie the Girl. The girl is now rubbing the flank of the beast while Pete is trying to draw a blood sample.

But no! the whale is alarmed! She breaks away with wires and rubber tubing in wild disarray. She circles and lifts her body . . . *swoosh!* The scientists are drenched; they laugh. They have, they think, enough data. If any bits are lacking they will try again; perhaps next summer, when their co-worker Susie is back to help them.

The thermistor moving aft in the whale's inner parts keeps up its monotonous *beep-beep-beep.*

In the last week of August the Little Calf and his mother are feeding on the great and deep Pacific, halfway between San Francisco and Oahu, a thousand miles from nearest land. Remote indeed they are, but not lonely, for never are they out of range of the submarine voices of their own kind.

The final day of the year of the whale is a climax to a normal year of life in which adventure is mingled with routine, and stress is intertwined with rest, and food is paced with hunger.

Today at dawn the mother and calf begin to hear again the familiar sounds of their lesser relatives, the porpoises. But now they hear new sounds as well: the steady throb of a tuna ship (a purse seiner) and the echoes bounding from the plump

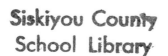

bodies of a thousand tunas—yellowfin and skipjack. The tur-
moil centers around a fishing scene that the mother could not
have known ten years ago, for it is a modern scene. The inven-
tion of lightweight nylon netting and powerful hydraulic net-
hauling machines has led the fishermen to abandon hand-
lining in favor of purse-seining. Now mother and calf see at a
distance, but do not comprehend, the capture of a hundred
tons of fish in one great sweeping haul.

The blue-gray ship moves swiftly toward a choppy circle
of the sea: a sea all torn with the rushing bodies of tunas and
porpoises feeding together in a tight group three hundred
yards across. The ship circles the melee, assisted by two swift
launches that concentrate the animals as a cowboy surrounds
the cattle in his charge. A half-mile net is dropped astern, then
the ship backs down to let the porpoises, but not the fish, escape. Seven porpoises, though, fail to jump the net; they are
confused and frightened; they tangle in the folds and drown.
The fishermen chop their sleek bodies from the webbing and
drop them over the side. The purse net tightens and the great
bright leaping fish, cold-eyed, pour onto the deck. They flail
briefly and die, staring. The catch is over in two hours.

As the year ends, the form of the Little Calf leaves a thin
track on the flat immensity, a swirling punctuation, a blend of
liquid and life. A cool wind moves. The red light gleams on the
wave at his brow. Then the sun sinks below the sea, and the
tiny whale is gone.

About the Author

Victor B. Scheffer specialized in the study of marine mammals as a biologist with the United States Fish and Wildlife Service in Seattle, Washington, from 1937 to 1969. He has lectured at the University of Washington on wildlife ecology and on the natural history of vertebrates. He received his Ph.D. from the University of Washington in 1936, is a member of Sigma Xi and Phi Beta Kappa, and received the United States Department of Interior's Distinguished Service Award in 1965. Dr. Scheffer was awarded the John Burroughs Medal (1970) for the year's best book in natural history, *The Year of the Whale,* from which this book was adapted. His most recent book is *The Year of the Seal.*

About the Illustrator

Leonard Everett Fisher has illustrated over 100 books, including a number in the field of science; some of these he has written himself. A native New Yorker, he studied at the Heckscher Foundation, the Art Students League, and the studio of Moses and Raphael Soyer. He was awarded the Pulitzer Art Prize in 1950. In addition to the decorations for *The Year of the Whale* (which are included in *Little Calf*), Mr. Fisher provided the drawings for *The Year of the Seal.*